# The Art of Slowing Down

A Sense-Able Approach to Running Faster

Edward Yu

The Art of Slowing Down: A Sense-Able Approach to Running Faster

Copyright ©2010 by Edward Yu.

Photographs, including covers © Andre Andreev, www.loveyourportrait.com.

Edited by Julia Gillam. Assistant Editor: Ann Yu.

Cover Design by Andre Andreev, with help from Ann Yu and Edward Yu.

Assistant to Andre Andreev: Nick Kane

Models: Arlys Alford, Andre Andreev, Amanda Espy, Julianne Gale, Julia Gillam, Alex Geroulaitis and Edward Yu.

Library of Congress cataloging-in-publication data: contact publisher

Panenthea press, www.panenthea.com

266 F, N. Arlington Ave., Harrisburg, PA, 17109

Printed in the United States.

First Printing: October, 2010

ISBN 978-1-4507-4158-3

*For Mom and Dad
who always stood behind me.*

# Table of Contents

# Prologue

Fewer than 24 hours after my formal induction into the Masters' century-old Bagua lineage, I encountered my first reality check. I had just begun practicing when I heard Master Ge's cannon voice reverberating through the park where all the students had gathered that evening.

"That was completely terrible!" he shouted in a tone so filled with disgust that it was as if someone had insulted his entire family.

Somebody is really screwing up, I chuckled to myself as I continued my practice.

"Completely terrible!" Master Ge repeated.

I had never heard him this angry before and felt relieved that I had always been on his good side. Momentarily I imagined Master Ge as a great army general, commanding his troops with incredible tenacity and verve during the heat of the battle. I could hear his voice roaring like a howitzer over the cacophony of exploding gunpowder.

"Terrible!" he repeated a third time.

I wondered how Master Ge's decibel rating would compare to that of an idling metro bus. Obviously, somebody wasn't getting his point, though I didn't immediately see who, since I was several meters away, busily racing through the form. As usual, I was in a hurry to finish up because I wanted catch the last call at my favorite hole-in-the-wall restaurant down the street. The thought of steamed buns was suddenly making my mouth water.

"Stop!"

I would bet on Master Ge over the bus. Then nothing but a silence so eerie I couldn't resist turning to see what all the commotion had been about.

A momentary glimpse was all I needed to realize that somebody had been insulting his family—the family of Bagua masters who had carried the art through seven generations all the way down to the present moment. Seeing Master Ge squared off like an angry bull, ready to charge in my direction, I felt an instant jolt of both horror and utter disbelief.

Me?

As he brushed me aside and proceeded to mimic what seemed at once to be an exaggerated, yet oddly accurate rendition of my movements, I realized my insult. When the masters demonstrate the correct movement and then mimic yours it's like being handed plastic flowers after having just returned from the botanical garden. My form was indeed a cheap imitation, not simply because I was a relative beginner with thousands of hours of training ahead of me, but moreover because my distraction and lack of enthusiasm had evidently showed. Master Ge had caught me going through the motions and now that I was representing his lineage he had no patience for mediocrity.

At the tender age of 32, Master Ge's yelling marked the beginning of a 6-hour a day, 7-day a week training regimen during which I was to discover for the first time in my life what it means to have your heart and mind fully involved. On a cool spring evening in the industrial city of Tianjin, China, I was discovering what it means, in other words, to learn.

## How to Read This Book

*Try to forget everything you've learned as an adult—the things that limit your view of the world, your fears, your prejudices, your preconceptions. Try to rediscover what it is like to be a child with a sense of wonder, and innocence. And don't forget to laugh. Remember, children are strong, they are resilient, they are designed to survive. When you drop them, they tend to bounce.*

-Terry Gilliam

For those of you who are in a hurry to improve your running and don't have time to go through the philosophy and methodology contained in this book, please skip "Life," "More Life" and "The Rest of Your Life"—that is, Part I, Part III and the Epilogue. I suggest you read Part II ("Practical Matters"), or simply go straight to the lessons. There are 20 of them located in Appendix II.

As you continue to do the lessons regularly, you will begin to feel differences in your body that you may not have felt before, and you will rediscover a certain vibrancy that you long ago forgot existed inside of you. Each new feeling in your body will have the potential to make a profound impact not only in the way you run, but in your posture, in your gait, in the way you perform other activities—indeed, in everything involving movement. Each new feeling will, in short, begin to transform the way you live your life.

Some of you will discover that rather than living life, you've been trying to get it over with—as if living were more of a chore than a journey to be experienced fully, deep down inside of yourself. In this discovery you will realize that living itself is not the chore, but rather hurrying through life—what I call, "not quite living"—that makes our days seem harried and senseless.

For those of you with enough time for the main body of text, be playful—for it is in play that we learn the most. Skip pages and even chapters (I often do when reading books), or start at the end of the book and go backward if you want. Most of all, please slow down and take your time. I hope you will savor the newfound feelings and sensations in your body that come from doing each lesson the way you might savor the sunset, a good piece of chocolate, or perhaps a fine wine. This way you will do three things at once. First, you will actually enjoy yourself. Second you will learn more. And third by enjoying and learning more, your running will improve faster. Yes, you read it correctly: by slowing down and enjoying yourself, you will run faster, and you will run faster faster—or in other words, you will improve more rapidly. Conversely, if you plow through the lessons as if they were something to get out of the way, you will not only enjoy them less, but you will improve less—if you improve at all. Going too fast, in other words, will slow you down by hindering your learning.

But to tell the truth, getting you to run faster is not the real reason I wrote this book. There's something much deeper waiting for you between the pages. It exists in the pauses between sentences and in the wondering that will emerge between chapters. It's the gift that you may long ago have forgotten about.

# Foreword

*Was it possible that modern man might forget his relationship with the rest of the natural world to such a degree that he separated himself from his own heartbeat, wrote poetry only in tune with machines, and was irrevocably cut off from his own heart?*

-Margaret Mead

I began writing this book in the midst of teaching running classes where instead of showing students how to run, I had them roll around on the floor in slow motion. I mean this quite literally: in my classes, students roll around on the floor. And while they are rolling around, they are encouraged to listen to their bodies. That's all. Simply listen.

The funny thing is when you begin to listen, you start to hear things you haven't heard in a long time, and sometimes things that even seem very foreign. It's not that your hearing has been deficient all these years, but more likely that you haven't taken the time to hear. You see, hearing takes time. And listening means giving yourself the time to hear.

What the students heard came from a place deep inside themselves. Voices that had been shut out for a long, long time. Voices that if heeded could put them on a new path for living—a path toward greater power, coordination, balance, flexibility and pleasure. What students were hearing was the beating of their own heart.

## My Not-Quite-Life as a Runner

I myself am not a runner, though I ran track and cross country in high school and even completed a couple triathlons before turning twenty. Ironically, now that I no longer train for the sport, I can run faster and with much greater power and ease than when I was twenty-five years younger and running several miles a day. Now that I take my time to roll around on the floor, I have discovered that life arrives when I slow down. It is counterintuitive that speed, power, balance and coordination can all be linked to slowing down rather than speeding up. How could this be?

What I've discovered in the years since I stopped running is that power does not result from muscling your way through—the "no pain-no gain" sort of approach—but rather by taking your time to listen to what your body is telling you. You actually have to slow down in order to simply hear what your body is saying. There's really no other way.

Your body is speaking constantly. And the biggest difference between the great Olympic runners and the rest of us is not that they are somehow genetically superior, bench press more weight, or have more willpower. It's that they actually hear their bodies. Their hearing is so acute that they often notice the slightest whispers. We teenagers and adults, on the other hand, miss a great deal of what our bodies are saying and truthfully, we only stop to listen when we can no longer ignore our body's screaming, as in the case of an injury. Anything less and we claim not to hear it. But the truth is we can't hear because we don't listen. We've become caught in a vicious cycle of not listening and thereby corrupting the sensitivity of our hearing.

Imagine going to heavy metal concerts every weekend and standing right next to the loudest speakers. Eventually, you will lose the ability to make fine distinctions in sound. You will begin turning the volume on your own stereo higher and higher just to be able to distinguish what you once could effortlessly.

Life, for most of us has been some measure of attending heavy metal concerts. The stresses of everyday life have become the noise that blocks out the sounds coming from our bodies. The noisy thoughts in our heads telling us to go faster, work harder, be smarter, look more attractive, be more obedient, be more rebellious, wear this kind of clothing, drive that kind of car, work this kind of job...all of it plays like the blaring speakers in a concert. We have gotten to the point where we can no longer hear ourselves. In fact, we have given up even listening, by which I mean we have given up listening to our deepest sensations and feelings. We have in other words, become numb to our own hearts. They go on beating nonetheless, and we go on living, of course, but in a perfunctory way, as if life were something to be endured and survived. We do our best to "kill time" and "get it over with" and in the process, we unwittingly drag ourselves through the prolonged torture of getting through life rather than living it.

Yet through all this, our hearts continue to speak to us. After all these years they haven't forsaken us, but continue to wait for us hoping one day to be heard. In a sense, they have always been there to guide us to what we once knew. If you follow your heart, you will end up with more than you could ever imagine. But to know what your heart wants, you have to start listening.

## Why Start on the Floor?

The reason I often have my students start on the floor is because it reduces the number of distractions bombarding their nervous system. Notice how talking on the phone while driving changes the way you drive. Talking tends to distract you and in the process your driving suffers.

Each distraction to the nervous system occupies part of your mind, leaving less of it to pay attention to what you want to pay attention to. Getting off your feet frees up the part of your mind that keeps you upright when you're sitting or standing and allows you to pay much more attention to what you're doing. It's like turning down the volume of your stereo so that you can hear the wind blowing outside. In this case what you start to "hear" is the amount of effort you're exerting and the amount of discomfort or comfort you feel. When there is too much noise, you can't sense subtle gradations in either effort or discomfort. Everything is either loud enough to hear over the noise, or else you don't notice it. It's why people don't whisper at rock concerts. And it's why many of us have damaged our bodies over years without even realizing we were doing so. We have turned the volume up so high that we can't hear our bodies speaking. Some of us don't take notice until finally we've herniated a disc, torn ligaments, developed a debilitating physical condition, or collapsed from depression.

## Making Sense of Life

The disciplines that have been instrumental in showing me the power of slowing down are Feldenkrais—an ingenious method of learning how to learn—and the timeless Chinese martial arts of Bagua and Taichi. All three involve paying close attention to the sensations and feelings in your body so that you begin to notice how different parts of yourself can work cooperatively rather than in opposition. What we don't realize is that for the most part, we are not working in a unified, cooperative way with our own selves. This means that some parts of us are actually fighting against other parts. It is an internal battle of which we are largely unaware and the result can be anything from physical pain and injury to those disconcerting moments when something doesn't feel quite right but you can't put your finger on it. It can be subtle, like a barely noticeable tightness in your chest, or it can bear down on you and feel as if sandbags have been draped over your shoulders.

Improving sensory awareness is like dropping the sandbags, so to speak, thereby allowing you to move with more precision and power, which in turn, can lead to profound improvements in the way you run. More importantly, improving awareness can lead to greater enjoyment of the activity of running itself.

# The Art of Slowing Down

A Sense-Able Approach to Running Faster

# Part I:  Life

(You may want to skip this part if you are in a hurry)

# Chapter 1

# Running (and other things we want to get over with)

*I open my eyes and don't know where I am or who I am. Not all that unusual—I've spent half my life not knowing.*

-Andre Agassi

Years ago when I was a runner, my favorite part about running was sitting down after a race. Actually, it was virtually the only thing I liked about the sport since I found it to be torturously painful and at times, dreadfully boring. Obviously I didn't run because I enjoyed it. Yet the motivation to continue had to come from somewhere and in my case, a lot of self-esteem was wrapped up in doing well, being "fit," looking good and trying to be something that I wasn't. Like most teenagers—indeed, like most adults as well—I spent a lot of time trying to be rather than being, and believe it or not, this takes a lot of energy. As you will see later, trying to be requires forcefully restraining what is. It is as if two beings are inhabiting the same body: one being, and the other trying to be. In athletics, such internal conflict stifles speed, strength, coordination, balance and agility. Outside of athletics, such internal conflict stifles everything from creativity to spontaneity to your ability to deal with stress. So, where my trying to be made me run harder, it simultaneously stifled my running and my life outside of running.

I am not alone.

If you observe the posture of most people while they're running you will likely feel discomfort in your own body. Compare this to the feeling you have when you watch Olympic runners glide down the track. You can actually sense their power and effortlessness. It looks so easy. So why isn't it easy for the rest of us?

Running may be unpleasant or otherwise less than joyful for the same reason many of us find it uninteresting: we can't feel our own bodies. By this, I mean we have a general sense of effort and strain and maybe even endorphins flowing into our bloodstream from time to time, but we don't know what it feels like to have our entire selves working together in unison.

The primary difference between Olympic runners and the rest of us is not that they possess superior strength, endurance or willpower, but that they aren't busy sabotaging themselves. Unlike many of us, virtually all of their effort goes toward their intended purpose: moving forward swiftly. Much of our effort on the other hand, inadvertently goes toward slowing us down. It's like hitting the brakes and the accelerator at the same time, which may explain why our engine feels like it's straining.

Of course, acting this way does not make sense. And the reason it doesn't make sense is because we cannot sense what we are doing. We are unaware that we are literally fighting ourselves with every step.

## Turning the Doorknob

*"When you see somebody who can't type, they start with two fingers. If they go on typing like that, they won't gradually use ten fingers. They will get better and better at using this terrible method. The hands move very fast like a couple of mad hens. But they never develop a good technique and the result is that typing is always a strain and an effort."*

-Trevor Leggett

In modern society, grinding and straining have become the norm by which we measure our lives. Running is simply one aspect of this. "I guess I wasn't meant to be a good runner," I might say or perhaps, "Running isn't meant to be fun." I might begin to think that I'm not working hard enough. Doctors might tell me that aches and pains are simply part of the aging process (They won't say, however, that self-destruction is part of the aging process). Specialists might say that my knees (insert any body part you like—whatever part that hurts) weren't designed for such pounding and advise me to stop. They might even say that no knees or backs or necks were designed for such pounding. Of course they might be right, but has it occurred to them what the source of pounding is?

We are like a person in front of a door, pushing on the door, kicking it, pounding on it, knocking our heads against it, and doing everything but taking the easiest approach: simply turning the knob.

I know this because I am one of those who went for the conventional approach, enduring years of strenuous training in high school that continued for a couple years afterward when I competed in triathlons. Though I ran on a State Championship cross country team my senior year, and later placed well in triathlons, I almost never found running to be particularly easy or enjoyable. With rare exceptions, running remained drudgery and a major chore that I naturally did not look forward to. And it was symbolic for how I lived the rest of my life, slogging through what I thought was an endless struggle to attain that ever-elusive feeling of success.

Virtually all of us are striving for success and consequently, many of us end up doing things we really don't want to do. For those who suffer, this book is especially for you.

Some of us, on the other hand, spend our days doing mainly what we want to do. Some of us, for example, run because we are entirely in love with the activity. For those who love running, this book is especially for you.

Regardless of how much you suffer or how much you enjoy running, there is always time to slow down.

# Chapter 2

# The Hurried Runner, a.k.a. "The Bulldozer"

*Instant coffee is punishment for people who are in too much of a hurry.*

-Alan Watts

In order to stop fighting ourselves, and thereby unintentionally slowing ourselves down, we must be aware that we are actually doing it. And in order to be aware of it, we need to literally feel it. Feeling leads to awareness, and awareness leads to more speed, power and agility.

But how could the solution be so simple? You may be thinking, If it were that easy, we would all be great runners… wouldn't we?

Yes, we would, but we would have to reverse all the years of assimilation of our "hurry-up" culture in order for this to happen.

Hurrying is a symptom of modern society's fixation on accomplishment. It is a constant preoccupation that I need to be somewhere other than where I am, doing something other than what I am doing at this moment, being someone other than who I am. It is a major reason why many of us are not fully present in daily life, our attention wandering far away from us—into the past, or future.

You may think that running and walking are the perfect activities for people in a hurry. You may think that the way to improve is to hurry more—to use what I call, the do it faster, get it over with approach. And you will sense such attitudes in people scurrying past you on the street. Something about them says, "Don't get in my way because I'm in a hurry!" Interestingly, if you really pay attention, it is not their speed that cues you into their hurriedness. They may not even be traveling any faster than anyone else. There's something else—a certain characteristic which you can't put your finger, but which nonetheless registers as a feeling of dis-ease in your own body.

The renowned Bagua Master, Guoliang Ge used to say to me, "Your form should be beautiful. It should look unhurried, graceful, easy and effortless. It should not be painful to watch, putting observers into distress. If you put people in distress, you are not doing Bagua." When you watched Master Ge in action, you got a sense of awesome power, resulting from grace and effortlessness rather than a gnashing of teeth and straining of muscles. Because he was never in a hurry, his movements remained fluid and powerful rather than choppy and tension-ridden. What was more surprising to observers was that his unhurried attitude gave him tremendous speed and precision. Even highly trained martial artists half his age could not match his quickness and agility. When they made contact with him, they would, in a flash, find themselves lying on their backs.

## If You Can't Feel Yourself, Then You Can't Feel Yourself Feeling Good

*In well-made chocolate, the sweetness should highlight the cacao's natural complexity and bitterness the way it can when you add small amounts to a cup of good espresso. Excessive amounts of sugar will bring a big burst of sweetness and then…nothing. This hollowness is what makes the lack of flavor in low-grade chocolate so glaringly apparent. No wonder people eat whole bars of bad chocolate in a manner of minutes.*

-Zingerman's Guide to Good Eating

In a world where "time is money," emphasis on speed sabotages speed. It may seem like a contradiction, but it isn't. Great athletes, dancers, musicians, writers, scientists, educators and martial artists all know this. To them it is obvious. Albert Einstein never said, "If I don't finish the General Theory of Relativity by five o'clock my mother will never love me again!" Had the great Bagua and Taichi masters not given themselves time to make new discoveries, they would not have become masters, and consequently instead of their art and insight, we would have women and men, like us, too busy to take notice of life.

Hurrying is in one sense, commanding yourself to do something without paying attention to how you do it. This is why most people become rather clumsy and careless when they are rushed. They are unaware of where they are say, losing balance, or gripping excessively with their hands. This is because most people, when commanded to do anything, either by themselves or by others, will tend to strain and carry anxiety into whatever it is that they are doing. They will say, "Last time wasn't good enough, so this time I must try harder!" Of course, they may not say it audibly, or even consciously think it, but something about them is screaming, "Faster! Harder! More effort!"

The question is, who is really in command, or to put it another way, what part of you is trying, and what part is being tried? As you have surely noticed, your body has been answering this question all your life. It speaks to you through the tension you may feel in your neck and shoulders, the pain you may feel in your joints, the strain you may feel in your jaw, the tightening you may feel in your throat and chest, the tiredness you may experience when you are engaging in a particular activity. Its voice is also the feeling of openness in your chest, the ease you feel at certain times when everything seems to be going right, the joy you feel when partaking in activities you like. Of course, when you spend most of your time doing what you don't want to do, you may even forget how to feel good. You may reach a point early in life when fully letting go and feeling pleasure becomes very difficult. Strange as it may sound, most people I encounter have difficulty fully enjoying life because they have forgotten how to feel themselves. And if they can't feel themselves, they can't feel themselves feeling good.

And this brings us back to hurrying: when we hurry and thereby command ourselves to do something, what are we in fact doing? Do we really get the job done faster? Is it done well?

At each and every moment of our life, we have the possibility to discover something new. Great athletes know this intuitively and make use of this possibility in their work and often in their play—in fact their work often looks like play. Children too, understand this intuitively, which is why they tend to laugh frequently and learn much faster than adults.

Each infant, in fact, has an intimate relationship with discovery. Infants are constantly at play, discovering new movements and new relationships with the world. They take complete initiative for their own learning and if they did not, they would never crawl, much less stand up on their own two feet.[*]

## We Are Unaware That We Are Unaware

If you consider that there is an infinite number of ways to hurry, then looking at how you hurry can give you clues about what you're actually doing with your body. When you are in a hurry notice how much you see in front of you. How much of your environment do you notice through your eyes, ears, nose, touch? What happens to your breathing?

In general, the more hurried we are, the more we behave like the person

---

[*] In our culture, we often prod and push children to stand and walk before they are ready. We hurry them, in other words, to do what they would normally do if left to their own devices. "When parents have greater respect for the learning process of the young human being, for whom everything is strange and new, and they restrain their expressions of approval at the first signs of success—especially with regard to standing and walking, which are accomplishments vulnerable to distortion—the child can ripen in her own time and arrive at the ability to stand when she is better prepared and trained, and capable of continuing to refine the process as well. The child receives a firm foundation for her entire life, not only in the alignment of the spine, not only in the ease and comfort with which she relates to standing and to physical activity in general, but also in the sense that she has a better chance of growing and going through the obstacles of life forever free of having to earn love through actions which she does or does not perform. Such a lucky child could believe that being born is sufficient reason for being loved." –Ruthy Alon

who is so thoroughly frantic in looking for his car keys that he doesn't notice them sitting right in front of him. Were he to pause and breathe, he would see more of the complete picture. Being hurried, however, his vision will have narrowed sufficiently such that he will waste more time looking for what is staring him in the face. It seems ridiculous, but this is how most of us behave. We are unaware of the alternatives. And we are unaware that we are unaware.

## Sally's Story

*Not only do we have to be good at waiting, we have to love it. Because waiting is not waiting, it is life.*

-Josh Waitzkin, 8-Time U.S. National Chess Champion

Sally was an avid swing dancer who arrived in class one day complaining of chronic back and neck pain. She had come, not to run faster, but simply in the hope of finding a way to alleviate her suffering.

I started the students on their backs with some gentle rolling that allowed them to, among other things, discover and create connections between their feet, hips and spine. After a few minutes, Sally stopped and covered her eyes with her hands.

I had noticed that despite frequent suggestions to slow down and pay attention, she continued to race along hurriedly, as if afraid of falling behind. Rather than paying attention to herself, her eyes never left me as I walked around the room giving instructions. Meanwhile, her bird-like movements were done with a certainty that I see in many new students. It is a certainty that says, "Okay, I did it. Now what's next?"*

Certainty, whether in words or movement, not only communicates an attitude, but more importantly, solidifies beliefs and habitual movement patterns. When I am certain, I am saying to myself, "This is the way I do it," which is often simply another way of saying, "My way is the one right way to do it." If you have ever watched a political debate, or read a how-to book (for example, a book on running), then you know what I'm talking about. Because certainty avoids wavering, it can be very useful for getting the job done. But what happens if there is more than one way? What if there are other ways that actually work better?

## The Power of Awareness

When I was in school, most of us were busy trying to get the right answers. We were, in other words, trying to be right. But trying to be something also means trying not to be something else. What, you might wonder, were we

---

* Of course, the answer is, "nothing." For once you have cancelled out the present moment, that is all you are left with.

trying not to be?

Like all of us, Sally perceived a world filtered through her assumptions, one of which happened to be, "Gotta move fast and get it done!" Part and parcel of this assumption was a chronic clenching of her jaw, locking of her knees, holding of her breath and tightening of her fingers. She had unconsciously chosen these strategies to represent her "rightness."

Sally is not alone.

Most of us unwittingly choose such strategies to uphold our own rightness. And hold up we do, as if carrying sandbags over our heads. By this, I am not saying that holding ourselves "right"—or to put it another way, being self-righteous—is necessarily a bad thing, but rather that doing so may not always be in our best interest. Living in Los Angeles, for example, I might assume that I'm "right" to drive on the right side of the road. But if I unconsciously carry this "rightness" to London or Tokyo, I'll find myself facing in the wrong direction.

Were we to slow down and become conscious of it, we would realize that we always have a choice and that it might be a good idea to check the local traffic rules, so to speak. If we are married to the agenda of being right, on the other hand, we may never see the choice, rushing instead into oncoming traffic and wondering why everyone else is driving in the "wrong" direction.

## Our Unfamiliarity With Slowness

Eventually Sally slowed down enough to begin noticing her own patterns. One of the first she noticed while lying on her back was that she got dizzy and sometimes nauseous whenever she slowed down. Her nervous system—and her system was indeed, nervous—was so used to going at warp speed that gentle, slow movement had become something entirely alien and uncomfortable.

As a swing dancer you might think that Sally would have no problem performing slow movements. The assumption here is that slow movements are easier to perform than faster ones and that swing dancing with its fast, whirling steps would be more likely to make you dizzy or nauseous than lying on your back and gently rocking side to side. Yet in a culture that places a premium on going faster, it is more likely that its inhabitants are more accustomed to scurrying about at high speed than slowly and methodically exploring movement. In such a culture, anxiety runs rampant and people's movements tend to be linear, choppy and clumsy, rather than smooth, graceful and coordinated. If you consider that learning occurs through your sensory system, what we are teaching ourselves in our compulsion to "get it done," is how to be anxious, uncoordinated and clumsy. What we present to our minds is a version of balance and equilibrium that is ironically unbalanced and un-equilibrated. When imbalance and disequilibrium have become the norm, moving toward balance and equilibrium can initially provide a disturbing contrast to the nervous system.

# Chapter 3

# What Does it Mean to "Slow Down"?

*Please pay attention not just to the words, but to the silent spaces
between the words.
That's when the shift happens.*

–Eckhart Tolle

The greatest improvements in power, speed, coordination, agility and balance will occur when we slow down enough to become aware of the proverbial sandbags we are carrying. Slowing down allows us to become aware of what we were previously unaware of.

If this is the case, what does it mean to "slow down"?

The answer seems obvious, yet if we all knew, I would never have written this book and you probably wouldn't be reading it.

I have noticed in my years of teaching that when I ask new students to slow down, all of them, with very little exception, continue to move very quickly. Their idea of slowing down and mine are obviously not the same.

How slow is slow enough?

This question can be answered by another question: how slow do you need to go in order to discover something new? Consider that slowing down is simply a tool by which you can become aware of things that you were not previously aware of. And what you are not aware of is precisely what keeps you from running with more power.

This means that there is no set speed for the word, slow. The appropriate speed is determined by what it takes to feel and sense and therefore experience more at any given moment. And since circumstances change from moment to moment, pacing needs to change as well. In this regard, slowing down could translate to an endless search for the ideal pace for increasing awareness at any given moment. It is endless not because you never find what's appropriate, but because every moment is a new moment. The searching alone is what allows you to become more aware.

Another way of looking at speed is to view it from the standpoint of receiving information. The human nervous system is designed to handle an enormous amount of information—so much so that neuroscientists are still astonished by its processing abilities. Yet, while the amount that it can process appears to be almost limitless, the pace at which it can receive, or in other words, take in new information, remains limited. If too much information is dumped onto the nervous system at once, it will be lost. This is because entry into the nervous system is akin to getting water to pass through a bottleneck. If you attempt to pour a bucket of water all at once into a bottle, almost all of it will end up as a puddle on the floor. Similarly, if you present your nervous system with too much new information at once—something that tends to happen when you are moving quickly—the information will be spilled into the ether, so to speak, and you will have forsaken the opportunity for learning and improvement.

## Riding the Bullet Train

Imagine riding a bullet train and trying to observe objects that are within a few feet the tracks. If you're going too fast, all you will see is a blur, possibly making you dizzy, or even nauseous. When going at top speed—say, 200 miles an hour—nothing will be discernable. If the train slows down to 190 miles an hour, you will still see nothing but a blur. While it is true that your speed was just reduced by 10 miles an hour, the picture you are seeing will not be much clearer, if at all. Even if the train keeps decreasing its speed, it will take a considerable amount of slowing down before anything close to the window is discernable from anything else—that is, before you begin to even vaguely recognize what it is that you are seeing. Quite likely everything between 190 and 20 miles an hour will be too blurry to tell.  Perhaps at 20 you will start to be able to discern gross differences.  One moment, for example, you may think that you just passed a four-legged animal rather than a human. You may assume it's a dog because of its size, but truthfully, it could have been a leopard, a goat or a large piñata, considering that all you saw was a blurry mass with four leg-like attachments. The next moment you might know that you just passed a car rather than an elephant, but you still won't know the make or model.

When you approach 15 miles an hour things get much clearer relative to 20 miles an hour. But you will still miss details. Was that a man or a woman? Was the person wearing glasses? What did that sign say? As you approach slower speeds even more will become discernable. And it is only when you are on the verge of stopping that you may finally be able to read the print on a flyer, or notice the stitching on someone's sweater, sense the curve of a man's chin, notice the cracks in the cement, gaze at a spider web and possibly even locate the spider in it.

In our fast paced world, we are moving like a bullet train going at top speed—that is to say, way too fast for our nervous system to keep up with. In this manner we are depriving our nervous system of new information and therefore preventing ourselves from learning. Yet we continue to wonder why every time we look out the window we see nothing but blurry images. We may occasionally slow down, but have we slowed down enough so that we can actually perceive more of the world? And herein lies the catch: Even though going from 200 to 190 miles an hour is indeed slowing down, and going from 190 to 50 miles and hour is slowing down even more (a 75% decrease in speed!), it isn't nearly enough to catch what is right outside the window.

We are all conductors of our own bullet train. By not slowing down enough to make distinctions, we continue to bar new information from entering our nervous system and this leaves us repeating the same old habits that have prevented us from improving in the first place.

By slowing down enough so that we can discern differences, we let in new information and this in turn allows us to move away from our habits. In the case of movement, discernment comes through sensing and feeling. Can you, for example, sense how much effort it takes to lift your left leg compared to your right? Do you begin to tighten your chest or hold your breath as you slowly lifted your leg? Do you begin to wobble?

As you slow down more, you will begin to notice subtler and subtler changes. Like seeing the spider in the web, you will feel places where you were holding unnecessarily, but wouldn't have noticed had you been going faster. You will feel parts that have been overused and others that have been asleep and therefore not doing the work that they were meant to do. You will literally feel yourself in ways that you have not felt before. And it is in this increased sensitivity to your own movements that you will begin to run with greater power and ease.

# Chapter 4

# The Art of Learning:  You Already Have Everything You Need

*There is a vitality, a life force, an energy, a quickening that is translated through you into action, and because there is only one of you in all of time, this expression is unique.  And if you block it, it will never exist through any other medium and it will be lost.  The world will not have it.  It is not your business to determine how good it is nor how valuable nor how it compares with other expressions.  It is your business to keep it yours clearly and directly, to keep the channel open.*

-Martha Graham

For me, teaching running classes that involve little to no actual running is not contradictory, though it is anathema to the way I was "taught" to run. You see, most education is a process of a teacher, coach, parent, expert or even advertising agency trying to superimpose "correctness" or "rightness" on top of you. In film photography, when you superimpose one image on top of another, the original negative is not transformed in any way. This means that while the projected image may look different, it is only because you covered up the original with something else. Similarly, you could say that conventional education is to a large degree about covering something up, and unfortunately, that something just happens to be you.

The result of all of this superimposition is that, as we grow older, we become less and less aware of the original lying beneath everything else. This is based on our mostly unconscious and long held assumption that the original is not good enough—otherwise why would we bother covering it up? But what if the assumption is totally inaccurate? What if beneath all the layers rested something quintessentially perfect just waiting to be uncovered? If we looked at it this way, then all of our efforts might be akin to a museum curator trying to add highlights to the Mona Lisa in an attempt to make her more mysterious and beautiful, or a park ranger trying to bulldoze the Grand Canyon trying to make it grander.

Superimposition, though the predominant force in conventional education, is simply one of an infinite number of approaches to learning and improvement. Another possibility is a different sort of interaction that allows for the transformation of the student by drawing out what is already inside. Thus, instead of the teacher superimposing on the student and the student being taught by the teacher, the interaction becomes a process of discovery through self-discovery.

If we look in the dictionary, we find that the roots of education as discovery through self-discovery go back to antiquity. The English word, education, comes from the Latin word, educare, which means to draw forth. Contrary to what education has come to mean, its root presupposes everything you need is already inside you. The seeds of knowledge and wisdom, in other words, lie dormant in your very being. All you need is to find a process that allows them to sprout forth. When the learning process involves a teacher, I call it "educaring" because it is distinct from conventional educating.* In educaring the teacher helps to draw out the student's innate intelligence, and in doing so, the innate intelligence of both begin to emerge. Unlike conventional education, the teacher and student are then involved in an interactive learning process of give and take, more akin to a symbiotic dance than a covering up of one by the other. Rather than the teacher superimposing and the student being superimposed upon, teacher and student engage in a cooperative project of uncovering layers from the original, so to speak.

As you may have already suspected, learning does not require the physical presence of a teacher (if it did, there would be little point in independently exploring the lessons in this book) even though it can sometimes be very helpful. This is because in educare, a teacher—or educarer—serves mainly as an observer and acts as a mirror of sorts, to assist in the student's own learning process. The educarer, in other words, helps the student see parts of herself that she did not see before. Obviously, if you, the reader, are willing, patient and observant, you can and will fulfill this role on your own. In fact, you may have already taught—or educared—yourself if you skipped ahead to the lessons. The degree to which you took your time and patiently observed your sensations is the degree to which you began to uncover your own genius.

## Wonder

*Normal adults never stop to think about such concepts as space and time. These are things children ask about. My secret is I remained a*

---

\* I am borrowing the term, educare, from magnificent early childhood educator, Magda Gerber. The enormous success of her educational—or perhaps more accurately stated, educaring—centers gives potent testimony to the notion that true learning does not occur by having someone, namely a teacher, impose something on someone else, namely a student.

*child. I always asked the simplest questions. I ask them still.*

-Albert Einstein

Uncovering your own genius—or, in a word, learning—is simpler than you might expect. It involves two components: wonder and observation. If you want a direct experience of your own genius, try Lesson 9 ("Where Does My Arm Begin?") before reading further.

Those of you who explored Lesson 9, may have noticed that just by wondering, your state of attention began to shift, making it possible to feel and therefore uncover more of yourself. The state of wonder is optimum for learning because it works to uncover layers of superimposed thoughts and movement habits that have been preventing you from sensing and feeling. Wondering and observing detach you from your habits and in the process, actually sharpen your ability to sense and feel.

Knowing this, it may not surprise you that wondering is a state used by wine tasters to fully appreciate the impact that wine has on their senses. By cultivating their sense of smell and taste over time, wine tasters can differentiate flavors to extraordinarily subtle degrees.

What about other disciplines? Consider that wine is just a metaphor for life and that our bodies are like fine wines waiting to be fully sensed and enjoyed. Bagua and Taichi masters are the great "samplers" of the human body, being able to differentiate extremely fine degrees of muscular effort the way wine tasters differentiate flavors and aromas. The masters can in fact discern body alignment and muscle tension to such minute levels that they are able to make themselves as heavy as a boulder in one instant, and as light and ethereal as a smoke in the next.

## If It Ain't Broke...

*Imagination is as effortless as perception, unless we think it might be "wrong", which is what our education encourages us to believe. Then we experience ourselves as 'imagining', as 'thinking up an idea', but what we're really doing is faking up the sort of imagination we think we ought to have.*

-Keith Johnstone

Educaring posits that there is actually nothing wrong with you and therefore nothing that needs to be fixed. It also assumes that learning occurs naturally, or in other words, when you are not trying to learn. Contrary to popular belief, trying to learn not only does little to help the process, but often blocks it. Attempting to do something that would happen anyway—that is, without your insistence—is like trying to aid a dolphin by attaching fins to its tail and scuba gear to its back.

Learning, in other words, has less to do with trying to make something happen, and more to do with allowing it to occur. The process of allowing new ideas and possibilities to arrive, rather than impatiently trying to force them into existence, is the same one that many great athletes use. By not fixating on achievement, the great ones actually achieve much more. By trusting the process, and not trying to make something happen, they know that something profound will arrive.

# Chapter 5

# Intention

*Can you imagine tying wrist and ankle weights around an infant so that he becomes stronger? Or stretching a baby's body into different positions to make her more flexible? This is the way we start to treat ourselves by the time we are in our late teens. Learning to become an adult often means learning to perform dull, repetitive routines instead of holding on to the active curiosity and exploratory movements of our youth.*

-Frank Wildman

If you consider that all of us mastered the act of running sometime in childhood, how do we account for our differences in speed, power and fluidity? How do we account for world-class runners being world-class and the rest of us not being world-class? When we watch great runners on television, there is normally some quality in their stride that we would like to possess but that we can't quite identify. And because we can't put our finger on what they are doing to run with such power and grace, we have little choice but to simply continue running the way we have always run. That is, we have little choice but to simply practice our particular manner of running.

So we practice. And we practice more. And we try harder. And in the end, our endurance, willpower and even times may improve, but the way we run is still basically the same. By practicing what we already know, we haven't learned anything fundamentally new.

This is not to say that the way we run is wrong, or that we are to blame for our lack of learning. Rather, what I am saying is that compared to learning better mechanics, working on endurance and willpower will do little if anything to help us understand what it is that makes great runners run with such phenomenal speed and power. Put another way, short of learning more mechanically efficient ways to use our bodies, we may improve our endurance, but we will not improve the way we run. And it is primarily the way Olympic athletes run that gives them the speed and power that we so desire.

## The Crucial Difference

Over the years I have noticed that most expert advice on improving running covers two basic formulas: 1) following the latest training regimen and, 2) working on technique. In advocating these, however, the experts unwittingly make a false assumption: practice what you already know and you will get better.

This statement is false because neither changing your training regimen, nor following technical advice addresses the learning that must take place if you are to run with more mechanical efficiency. And the statement is unwittingly false because, technical advice, while attempting to address body mechanics, is often too difficult to accurately follow (more on this in Chapter 10 [Following Instructions: Where Do My Knees Begin?]).

Surprisingly, even the simplest sounding instructions are normally too complicated, vague or ambiguous for people to follow with any accuracy. The result then is that, even when heeding the experts, we usually end up practicing what we already know—that is, we end up practicing all of the mechanical habits that have prevented us from fundamentally improving in the first place.

Of course, it can still be beneficial for us to work on endurance and willpower. But endurance and willpower are still separate issues from body mechanics. And there are strict limitations as to how far you can improve if you are not addressing the latter. These limitations are why mechanical efficiency, or to put it more simply, *power*, is the crucial difference separating great runners from good ones and good ones from their average counterparts.

## Are You Motivated by One and Only One Intention?

One way to understand the vital role that mechanics plays in running is to examine the role of intention. The critical difference between Olympic runners and most of the rest of us is that for Olympians, virtually all of their effort goes toward their intention of moving forward. Most of us, on the other hand, unwittingly devote a large amount of effort toward contradicting ourselves, thereby making our bodies heavier and slower. In fact, most of what people call "inability" whether in running or any other discipline, could be thought of as ability which has been unconsciously sabotaged. This is to say that anything less than highly efficient movement—a powerful stride in the case of running—has little if anything to do with genetics, endurance, fitness level or willpower, and everything to do with what we unwittingly do to block ourselves. Yes, you read it correctly: our lack of power is our own doing—or perhaps more aptly put, it is our undoing.

Stated another way, lack of power is more a result of conflicted intention otherwise known as self-sabotage, rather than any of the other factors previously mentioned. Contrary to its conventional definition, intention is not cut-and-dried, but rather something that can actually be clarified and refined. The difficulty in realizing this is that much of our intention lies beneath the level of consciousness so we are only aware of what remains above the surface, in our conscious mind. This means that while we may have one conscious intention—say, to run as fast as possible—beneath the surface, there may be many other conflicting, parasitic forces. Unfortunately, the conflict plays out in our bodies as if we are at war with ourselves, the possible result being postural defects, mechanical inefficiency, pain or injury.

If, for example, we examine how the average person runs, we will discover places where she unconsciously collapses her body. These are places where muscles seem to be asleep. As this is going on, parts of her that are not sleeping have to perform double duty to make up for the parts that are sleeping. But mechanical efficiency relies on all parts working cooperatively, and in unison. Not only is the sleeping part not participating, it's getting in the way, like dead weight. So our average runner has to carry it around like a sack of gravel.

Examples of conflicted intention can be observed not just in running, but in daily life where many of us are wanting to stay alert, pay attention and do good work, yet remain unable to do so even with the aid of drugs, the threat of punishment, or the reward of something such as a paycheck. The fact that even those who are considered productive rely on coffee, nicotine or other drugs to get them through their average day indicates that even the best of us are often burdened with conflicted intention. This is to say, when we are unable to perform as smoothly as we would like, something is happening beneath the level of conscious intention that is driving us down. Thus, to go back to the previous example, if our conscious intention to stay alert and perform well does not match the fact that we are often sleepy, apathetic and distracted, then our unconscious intention is probably doing something to undermine our efforts.

## Unintended Self-Sabotage

From a purely neuromuscular point of view, unrefined intention is manifest in two ways. First, it appears in the phenomenon I described above in which parts of us are habitually sleeping. In this case, certain muscles remain hypotonic, or overly flaccid when at rest, and underused when performing an action. Second, it appears in what Dr. Moshe Feldenkrais called parasitic muscle contractions, where certain muscles remain hypertonic, or overly contracted when at rest, and overused when performing an action.

In either case, unrefined intention acts like the defense of the opposing team in a football game in that it diverts force to where you don't want it to go. In football, the running back wants to take the ball straight down the field to score, but every member of the defense is trying to stop her. Each is a barrier around which she must travel in order to move forward.

From a biomechanical standpoint, I am the host organism to my own parasitic muscle contractions, all of which serve to both absorb and misdirect force, and thereby disrupt my coordination, balance and strength. Even though my conscious intention is to move forward, some of my unconscious intention drives me in other directions. Aside from the extra burden of work this places on me, some of the force inevitably ends up getting stuck in my joints causing torsion and compression, otherwise known as, undue wear and tear. At the same time because parasitic tension constricts the flow of everything from blood, lymph and oxygen to various waste materials, a good portion of my effort is not only inadvertently self-defeating on a biomechanical level, but self-destructive on an organic and cellular level.

## The Two Principles of Movement

Parasitic contractions in any part of your body will inhibit the smooth translation of force throughout your entire body. Chronically tense backs, shoulders and necks, for example, inhibit fluid and powerful strides that we see in world-class athletes. Even tight fingers, or a tight jaw will to some degree inhibit powerful and fluid movement in the rest of the body. This is why good boxers keep their hands loose and only clench their fist at the last moment, just as they are making impact.

To understand how parasitic contractions sabotage movement, we need to look into the following two fundamental principles of movement: 1) for every action, there is an equal and opposite reaction, and 2) your mind controls your muscles.

The first principle, sometimes known as the action-reaction law, comes from the preeminent physicist, Isaac Newton. When we apply his principle to biomechanics, we discover that contracting any muscle in your body automatically pulls your center of mass and therefore, your entire body in a certain direction. This means that your entire body is influenced by every single contraction of every single muscle fiber contained in it, which makes obvious sense when you think about it. Muscles pull and that pull must have a direction. Of course, we need pulling in order to move about. But what if we are pulling in unwanted directions and consequently pulling ourselves off-balance and therefore off-course? Then we have to expend added energy to keep ourselves in balance and on course so that we don't end up falling, or traveling in the wrong direction.

Every movement you make involves your entire body. Even if you only intend to move your left pinky, its movement is part of a larger neurological pattern encompassing your entire body. This is because muscles that are not obviously involved in moving your pinky are still active even if you are not aware of it. Each muscle fiber is, in fact, constantly firing to one degree or another. A muscle that is always contracting too much, is chronically short and tense. A muscle that never contracting enough is chronically long and flaccid. Of course, muscles do not contract by themselves. They are connected to a brain and nervous system that issue the executive orders, so to speak.

What differentiates Olympic runners from others is that they are able to contract some 630 muscles to precisely the right length at precisely the right time. The shortening and lengthening of each and every muscle in their body is coordinated in such a way that they are able to maximize propulsion while minimizing resistance. Olympic runners, in other words, are much more precise in controlling their muscles. They exhibit far fewer parasitic muscle contractions because when it comes to running, there is far less unconscious self-sabotage.

Moving with speed, strength and agility requires coordinating all of the muscular contractions throughout your entire body in a precise fashion. No muscle can pull too much or too little at any given moment. To accomplish such precision, your brain and nervous system have to monitor each and every muscle cell in order to adjust its pulling to just the right amount of contractive force at just the right time. Quite an extraordinary feat if you consider how many millions of muscle cells inhabit the human body. If speed, strength, and agility are proportional to how precisely your brain and nervous system coordinate the contraction of each and every muscle cell in your body, then sharpening your mind and removing parasitic intention should play a major role in training.

The question then is how do you sharpen your mind so that it is able to coordinate your muscles more precisely?

# Chapter 6

# Have You Lost Your Senses?

*In our particular culture…our initiatory rite begins at the moment of birth when, typically, we take the child away from the mother and put it in a sterile environment. The rite continues with early weaning and the taboo on sucking, and culminates in the drama of toilet training. These three separative efforts are initiated much sooner in our culture than in others. They help to create a continuum of self-imagery which denies the discontinuous, pulsating life of the body. They lead to acceptance of an artificial schedule, a socially imposed rhythm that kills individual rhythmicity. Wake up at 8. Brush your teeth at 8:05. Eat your breakfast at 8:10 and out the door. Catch the bus at 8:20. Go to school 9 to 5.*

-Stanley Keleman

For three hundred years Western Civilization has taken a reductionistic view on humanity, behaving as though the human mind were nothing more than grey matter sloshing between our ears. We have been acting, in other words, as if the gelatinous stew resting in our cranium operates independently from the rest of our body and is therefore capable of functioning normally without any connection to feeling, sensing or emoting. In this manner, our emotionless Spock-like mind controls our machine-like body:  our brain, which is like a test tube of biochemicals to be titrated, manipulates our body, which is like collection of joints to be resurfaced and "parts" to be stretched, replaced, cauterized, radiated or simply extracted.

This way of viewing the mind and body treats the human whole as collection of discrete parts that function with little or no relation each other. A foot problem, for example, is generally not thought to be related to the way you use your knees and hips, much less the way you carry your head. In this case, the foot is considered the sole cause (no pun intended) of its problems. As a result, surgeons may saw off bunions, fuse joints, reconstruct arches and prescribe pain-killers, but nobody seems willing to address the elephant in the room: how do the mind and body connected to that foot relate to its use or misuse? And, just as important, how does the movement of that foot relate to the use or misuse of the rest of the body?

In reality, the health and performance of each and every part of your body depends on the performance of each and every other part. Your overall health and performance, in other words, is related to whether or not your "parts" are working cooperatively.

## Mind-Body Unity

When people hear the word, measuring instrument, they will likely picture digital scales, calipers, volt-meters, or perhaps some high tech device with flashing lights. As a runner you might picture a heart-rate monitor, pedometer or calorie counter. Few, however, will consider the most powerful instrument of them all. Perhaps because it is hidden inside each and every one of us, theoretically not for sale.

Even with major advances in technology over the last half-century, engineers have yet to design a machine capable of walking, much less running, with the power, speed, agility and elegance of humans. And the enormity of the task makes it unlikely that they ever will. As we shall see in Chapter 10 ("Following Instructions: Where Do My Knees Begin?"), the mechanics of the human body are in fact, so complex, that they require an instrument far more powerful than the most advanced supercomputer to govern them. To achieve the kind of elegant and powerful movement that we see in Olympic athletes requires a mind that is not Spock-like, and a body that is not machine-like. It requires a mind and body that are one and the same.

Not surprisingly, the reductionistic way of viewing life has led to people moving more and more like machines—that is, in a choppy and linear rather than smooth and spiraling manner. The majority of contraptions in health clubs, for example, are designed to isolate body parts so that rather than creating fluid, full-body movement, they inadvertently train you to move in a jerky, robotic fashion. While this may be useful for increasing muscle mass, it has the unfortunate effect of making you less coordinated and agile.

It is of note that prior to the introduction of reductionistic principles, people from both East and West, did not separate the mind and the body. Perhaps this is why for millennia, the Chinese have used the same character to represent both mind and heart. According to the Chinese, sensing, feeling and thinking all involved not just your mind, but your heart as well. Thus, the character for "thinking" and the one for "sensing and feeling" both contain the heart-mind radical. The ancients believed that we did our sensing, feeling and thinking with one and only one organ.

In the last twenty years, cognitive and neuroscientists have finally "proven" the unity of mind and body. Having finally discarded the reductionistic paradigm, they now know that the mind's ability to refine movement by coordinating some 630 muscles with greater precision—a process otherwise known as learning—is inextricably linked to the body's ability to sense and feel. After three centuries, Western Science has returned to the age-old concept that the mind is something much deeper and all-encompassing than cold synapses firing between your ears.

As we shall see in the following chapters, your mind has the potential to sense and feel at extraordinarily subtle levels and in the process direct your movement with the precision of an Olympic athlete, concert pianist or Bagua master. Each of us can choose to move toward that potential or away from it by either developing or suppressing our sensibility—that is, our sense-ability. When we suppress our sense-ability, we begin to lose just that: our ability to accurately sense and feel. In the process, we sacrifice not only coordination, strength, balance and agility, but something even more fundamental.

The less we choose to sense and feel on our own, the more we must rely on external sources to do the sensing and feeling for us. Put another way, the less precisely we can direct ourselves, the more we end up relying on someone else to do the directing for us. We may, for example, rely on a heart rate monitor to tell us how hard and long to exercise. We may trust calorie counters to tell us how much to eat. We may rely on fashion magazines to tell us how to look. And we may look to running experts to tell us how to run.

Yet, each of us has the potential to leapfrog past experts and other external sources if we only pay attention to what is deep down inside of us—that is, if we start cultivating, rather than suppressing our sense-abilities. When you cultivate your sense-ability you are in effect connecting with your heart and thereby cultivating your mind. And a sense-able mind is not only the best, but moreover only instrument capable of guiding you toward your vast potential. There are no substitutes. The more you dull your sense-abilities, the more you blunt the very instrument designed to lead you toward improvement.

## How Did We Lose Our Senses?

*[W]hat we call upbringing or education is a way of making children conform to the conventions of society… [I]n the process, most children are—perhaps unavoidably warped. They lose their innocence and their spontaneity, their unselfconsciousness. In psychological jargon, they possess all kinds of inner conflicts and complexities, and they do not seem to be able to recover from them in adult life without the expense of psychoanalysis or some similar kind of therapy. And even*

*then, I am not quite sure how often they really recover.*

-Alan Watts

Losing our senses begins early in life because doing so allows us to get along. To one degree or another we must comply with parents, teachers, bosses—in short, authority, in order to make it through childhood, school and later, the working world. Think about this: what typically happens to children when they don't obey their parents and teachers? What happens to adults when they don't obey their bosses? What happens if you don't file your income taxes?

This is not to say that everybody always obeys to authority. Sometimes we exhibit a healthy disregard for people, organizations, or even ideological constraints that may be squelching our inner sanctum. We may, for example, leave a school, job or even profession that does not suit us. Mostly, however, we are playing a survival game called, "fitting in." Whether we are trying to be in with the "in" crowd, or the "out" crowd doesn't matter. The simple fact that we are trying to be something means trying not to be something else. It means turning off our senses to some degree and suppressing essential parts of ourselves.

Fitting in is not, in and of itself, intrinsically bad. Without some compliance to those around us we would have no culture and arguably, no human race. Too much compliance, however, and we end up with a society of automatons, with no connection to the beating of their own heart.

Look at the clothes you're wearing, the kind of haircut you're sporting and the things hanging on the wall in your home and you instantly know to which club you either belong or are trying to belong. Perhaps more striking, notice when something inside you reacts to the way another person is dressed. That something inside is saying, "I'm definitely not in that club!" Each club, whether the British Royal Family, Hell's Angels or the "I don't belong to any club" club has characteristic codes of behavior—or in other words, characteristic codes of moving. The question is how well do the movement dictates of your club really suit your individual desires and needs? How much does moving the "right" way mean cutting you off from your own senses? How much have you distanced yourself from the beating of your own heart?

Compliance taken too far means moving in a way that is not in accord with who you are. And when you are not in accord with who you are, you are literally uncomfortable, because while your body desires to move one way, you are forcing it to move another. You are busy trying to be what you are not and this contradiction can be literally felt in your body. Yet because your body does not stop talking, the only way to live with this contradiction is to ignore the language of your body, namely sensing and feeling. Living in contradiction means, in short, disabling your sense-ability.

# Have You Lost Your Mind?

*[E]ach of us masters any particular activity, from eating to playing the piano to performing surgery, by prolonged repetition of specific muscular patterns. By developing some muscles and leaving others partially or virtually totally unused, the repetition slowly determines the relatively stable relationships among the large segments of our bodies: a characteristic tilt of the head in relation to a slant in the shoulders, a turn in the pelvis manifested in a characteristic gait, a slight compression in the chest or a curvature in the back.*

*But within an authoritarian atmosphere these repetitions carry seeds of corruption. The practice necessary for skill is done in a context that rewards conformity to someone else's ideas rather than finding one's own way. The infant is permitted its brief moment of trial and error before learning that there are right and wrong ways of doing things. Doing things "right" becomes more important than learning....*

*...the naturally experimental infant is slowly educated into becoming an adult who is afraid of trying anything new.*

-Don Hanlon Johnson

As I mentioned earlier, your magnificent measuring instrument, capable of feeling and sensing to extraordinary levels of subtlety doesn't just reside in the grey matter between your ears. It actually encompasses your entire body. It exists in your left little toe, and in your right elbow; in your liver and in your large intestine; in your blood vessels and in your lymph nodes. Because sensing and feeling occur throughout your body, your mind lives everywhere in it. This is why some people refer to the body and mind as the "bodymind."*

It follows that when you begin to lose your senses, you also begin to lose your mind, which doesn't mean you are going insane. It simply means that you are not in touch with your own sense-abilities. Since sanity is defined by how the majority of people behave in society, you could say that losing your mind has actually become the norm—our cultural standard, in other words, of sanity. This being the case, people who maintain their sense-abilities and therefore don't lose their minds are ironically considered at least a little insane.**

Not surprisingly, our "sane" culture, which encourages and sometimes even enforces the muting of our sense-abilities exacts a heavy price from its in-

---

\* Ken Dychtwald has authored a pioneering book on the subject aptly entitled, *Bodymind.*

\*\* Given this, it should be no surprise that those who forge deeper connections with their senses are often thought to be at least a little crazy even though they form the ranks of every society's innovators and pioneers.

habitants in the form of deadening our innate curiosity and aliveness, inhibiting learning and improvement, and actually encouraging self-destructive tendencies. Our "sane" culture, in other words, encourages a great deal of mindless behavior.

How does this happen?

Just as muscles begin to atrophy when you don't use them, senses begin to dull when you ignore them. Since losing your sense-ability means losing your ability to distinguish between what feels good and what doesn't, it also means losing your ability to distinguish between what is good for you and what isn't.

Nature has equipped all living creatures with the ability to distinguish between what feels good and what doesn't in order to give all forms of life the maximum chance for survival. Without this ability, they literally begin to self-destruct. People who lack ability to feel pain, for example—such as those suffering from Hanson's Disease—will unwittingly cause so much damage to themselves that they eventually become disfigured. NFL football players perform a similar task when they are given painkillers or smelling salts for serious injuries and then sent back on the field (Here, it is not only considered sane, but heroic to sacrifice your body in an effort to win). Until recently, the media reported so little on the condition in which these athletes found themselves after leaving the gridiron that most of the public mistakenly believed they led normal lives.

For the rest of us who aren't in the NFL or suffering from Hanson's disease, we nonetheless play similar, albeit less dramatic roles in hurting ourselves. How could we not when we have lost our senses?

While just about everybody understands the feeling of acute pain, many of us have lost the ability to clearly distinguish between other sensations—namely ones that do not register as acute pain. Many of us, in other words, tend not to notice lesser discomforts that nonetheless impinge on the quality of our movement, mood and well-being. On the surface, it may sound like a good thing to be able to ignore pain and discomfort—if only to save money on doctor's bills and trips to the drug store. But as I mentioned above, feeling pain and even minor discomfort is a necessary tool by which humans, and indeed, all living creatures keep from destroying themselves.

Whereas acute pain normally signals sudden trauma, subtler discomforts signal damage that is either imminent or in the process of occurring, albeit at a slower pace. So when we ignore minor discomfort, we are ignoring something that is either potentially or actively destructive.

## Yin and Yang: Why Pain is Important

If I am well practiced at blocking out as much pain as possible, I may eventually lose my ability to distinguish between subtleties of discomfort—and just as importantly, subtleties of comfort. If I continue to push myself to extremes of pain tolerance, I may reach a point where anything short of acute pain no longer registers. In such cases I will still be able to tell the difference between pulling a hamstring and not pulling a hamstring, or throwing out my back and not throwing it out, but gross distinctions are not enough to move, and therefore live the way I want to. All the distinctions that give me greater self-awareness and thereby provide me with more power, agility, coordination and gracefulness, will have been lost. What I will be missing, in other words, are not only the messengers alerting me of acute injury, but the extraordinarily rich and varied world of distinctions that lies between acute pain and its absence.

In our fast-paced, results-driven, "no pain-no gain" society, it is not only our ability to feel pain that we relinquish, but our ability to feel at all. And this means that by diminishing our ability to feel pain, we also diminish our ability to feel pleasure.

Chinese philosophers of antiquity divided the world into a duality of yin and yang—opposing phenomena that depend on each other to exist. Because yin and yang are mutually dependent halves necessary to create the whole of human experience, neither was considered to be good or bad. To have light, you must have dark. Hot exists only because there is cold. As I mentioned earlier, to have a mind, you must have a body. And pleasure exists because of pain. You cannot extinguish one without extinguishing the other.

I believe this is one of the reasons so few people enjoy running. Instead of taking heed of pain, they try to suppress it. And in doing so, they minimize the possibility of feeling pleasure.

Here's how it works.

If I force myself to run regularly even though I don't like running, it's probably because I don't derive much pleasure from the activity. What I will clearly notice is the discomfort that comes from running—perhaps the burning of muscles, the exhaustion, tiredness, and maybe even the tweaking of parts of my body to which I am unwittingly causing injury. If I continue to plow my way through the discomfort, relying on willpower to carry me through, then I am not paying heed to my discomfort. I am probably blocking it out—perhaps even listening to music at the same time so as to distract myself from the pain. Each time I will my way through this process, I am ignoring the voices inside me saying things like, "this is unpleasant," or "this hurts." Obviously, I am not increasing my discomfort (at least not until I finally incur a major injury), but I am also not increasing the minute amount of pleasure I am getting in the process.

What, if on other hand, I started listening to my senses and feelings? I might then want to slow down. Initially I might not run as far. I might start my run by walking. I might even notice how I was pushing off my right foot and how that differed from how I pushed off my left foot. When I felt discomfort, I would likely change what I was doing, experimenting with ways that might make me feel better.

In the process of listening, I would start to know who I am and be able to compare it to who I was trying to be—someone in a hurry to get the run over with. I would begin to understand how I was running, and that awareness alone could help to guide me toward a better way of running. The act of feeling and sensing myself instantaneously creates new neural pathways, and this means new movement possibilities. While it is likely that I might go slower at times, run fewer miles and even revert to walking from time to time, it is also more likely that I would discover how to run faster and with more pleasure. And if running started giving me more pleasure, I would likely end up running more than I did when I wasn't paying attention to my feelings—not that getting yourself to run more should be your goal.

Let's compare your average runner to your average child running around on the playground. The average runner slogs her way through at a steady pace and often a grimace on her face. The average child on the playground varies her pace—sometimes sprinting, sometimes walking, sometimes darting, sometimes leaping, sometimes lying down and sometimes squealing with delight. Which one seems to have more energy? Who ends up running further? If you watch children (particularly those who haven't been introduced to video games), their energy seems boundless. They could run around on the playground for hours without tiring. We, on the other hand, often feel tired even before we take our first step. I believe this is because children pay attention to discomfort. They either avoid it or find ways to mitigate it. They also pay attention to pleasure and actually seek it out. They walk when they want to walk, and sprint when they want to sprint. In fact, it is in slowing down and walking, that they gain the desire to run and sprint—not because they are in a hurry, but because the human mind likes variation and stimulation. Running is a wonderful variant to walking. It is the yang to the yin of walking.

I have played enough basketball, tennis and soccer to know that people inherently like to run. But they like it only when it brings them pleasure. You will find that many of the fittest basketball, tennis and soccer players don't like the sport of running, even though during a game or match, they actually run more than most runners. All they need is a ball to chase and they're off to the races. By chasing a ball, they are chasing their pleasure. And as a runner, this is what you could be doing:  following your pleasure.

# Chasing Waves

A game I like to play when I go to the ocean is something I call, "chasing waves." As the tide goes out, I shuffle as a boxer would toward the receding water. As a wave starts crashing toward the shore, I wait until the last minute and then shuffle or simply run as fast as I can away from the water. Depending on how large the wave is, I give myself more or less distance from its shoreward crashing.

A nice element of this game is that there is so much possibility built into it. Depending on both the time of day, month and year, the tide will be closer to shore or further out, the waves consequently rolling in faster or slower. This means that along with the variation in speed, I'm dealing with a variation in grade because the slope on which I'm chasing and being chased is either flatter (when the tide is lower) or steeper (when the tide is higher). It also means that the sand on which I'm running is either firmer or looser.

On top of all of the environmental variation, I get to choose any number of ways to chase and be chased, often becoming thoroughly engrossed as I imagine a child would be, and all the while enjoying the sunshine, fresh air and ocean water. Meanwhile in my enjoyment, I am inadvertently strengthening my body—particularly since my toes ankles and metatarsals get to move in ways they normally wouldn't when encased in shoes and walking on concrete.

# Chapter 7

# To Be or Not To Be

*I hate tennis, hate it with all my heart, and I keep playing, keep hitting all morning, all afternoon because I have no choice. No matter how much I want to stop, I don't. I keep begging myself to stop, and I keep playing, and this gap, this contradiction between what I want to do, and what I actually do feels like the core of my life.*

-Andre Agassi

Seventh grade marked the end of my days of playing and exploring when overnight, boys my age seemed to have grown to twice my size and gained the power and speed to match. In an attempt to catch up with them, I began to abide by the principle of always pushing my limits. Looking back, it isn't surprising that by the time I turned fourteen I had already associated running with a great deal of pain and misery. Regardless of the fact that at one point I was winning junior varsity races, there was little joy to be had in either training or competing. And while it is true that I enjoyed a sudden spike in popularity during the brief time I was winning, the act of running itself remained for me, mostly drudgery. Later when the friends and attention disappeared—they tend to evaporate when your competition improves and you start coming in tenth place—I had to summon more willpower to continue.

By tenth grade, I was becoming increasingly unenthusiastic about lifting my head off the pillow when my alarm went off. On designated "hard" days when I knew our coach would be squeezing every last ounce of juice from our legs, I became sullen and irritable. At this point I was running with the varsity squad, and as its slowest member, barely able to keep up. The build up to races was even worse. Though it seems preposterous in retrospect, I distinctly remember warming up before many races with a sudden empathy for everyone who had ever been sent to the gallows.

School itself was simply another version of running in that those who struggled were simply encouraged to try harder. The problem, however, was not one of insufficient effort. With my short attention span and propensity to get caught up in the tiniest details, I would often find myself reading the same paragraph over and over. Each day felt like I was falling further behind.

Exhausted from running and unable to concentrate, I spent countless nights battling a desire to either catch a snippet of television or a snack from cupboard. Nine o'clock and still unable to figure out my first math problem, I would eat a bagel. Ten o'clock and I'd switch to physics:

> Centripetal force is a force that makes a body follow a curved path: it is always directed orthogonal to the velocity of the body, toward the instantaneous center of curvature of the path.

Huh?

Time to order a pizza. Two hours and a painfully bloated stomach later, my books continued to stare back impassively. If I was learning anything, it was how not to learn.

In the classroom things seemed equally complex. I often slept through chemistry and math, while in English my fear of looking stupid kept me on red alert and praying that the teacher wouldn't call my name. My classmates seemed impossibly smart as they rolled off expert, polysyllabic opinions on the 300-page Victorian novel we were supposed to have finished. In the two weeks we were given to read it, two dozen bagels, three pizzas and one trip to the gastroenterologist couldn't get me past page 22.

Obviously, trying harder wasn't working. Little did I know in high school, both learning and running can be joyful. By fixating too heavily on results however—be it the "right" answer, the good grade, or the faster time—I had taken the process out of the process and thus, the learning out of the learning.

Each day in cross country, for example, I would go to practice expecting to be in over my head. All the tension, anxiety and defeat revealed themselves, not only in the grim expression I carried through most of the day, but in my posture, which was a combination of over-tightness in certain areas and collapse in others. I had become an unwitting participant in my own oppression, piling sandbags on my own shoulders. My attitude, in other words, created a whole neuromuscular response that actually made my body feel heavier and my mind duller. Rather than living life, I was surviving it.

"Why did you continue on this way?" one might ask. "No sensible person would do this to himself!"

This is indeed true: no sense-able person would treat himself this way.

## Being vs. Doing

> If you think your life is about doingness, you do not understand what you are about. Your soul doesn't care what you do for a living—and

*when your life is over, neither will you. Your soul cares only about what you're being while you're doing whatever you're doing. It is a state of beingness the soul is after, not a state of doingness.*

-Neale Donald Walsch

You've probably noticed that the vast majority of practicing and training is more about getting results than about learning, more about getting the job done than how it gets done. For most people, practice means focusing on ends while letting the means slip far off into the background. In this manner, practice becomes more about trying to force the ends rather than allowing them to occur naturally. Neale Donald Walsch calls this doingness, and it stands in sharp contrast to beingness, which is about paying attention to and even enjoying the means by which we get things done.

You'll notice that people in modern society spend most of their energy and time on doingness. This is not necessarily bad. Doingness is how skyscrapers, homes and cars are built. It's how we get important things done, like putting food on the table. Doingness is vital because it is about survival.

Yet, what if there is more to life than simply surviving?

If I take a step back and ask not just what I am practicing, but how I am practicing what I am practicing, I begin to discover who I am being when I am doing what I am doing. And who I am being when I am doing what I am doing will actually determine the outcome of what I am doing. This is because being is shorthand for both being present and being myself.

Being present means being completely tuned in to what I am sensing and feeling. If as we saw earlier, sensing and feeling determines the quality of my movement, being present, which heightens my sensing and feeling, then enriches the quality of my movement.

As we shall see below, being myself is the act of knowing myself through sensing and feeling myself. So if I am being present and therefore completely tuned in to my sensing and feeling, then I am also being myself at the same time. To be present, in other words, is to be myself.

## Trying To Be Could Put You at the Bottom of the Ocean

Good runners get from A to B faster than average runners because they pay attention to their senses and feelings and consequently drop any parasitic tension that would otherwise get in their way. In other words, they improve the quality of their movement by sensing and feeling more and in this manner devote their efforts to being rather than trying to be good runners.

Average runners, on the other hand, try to be better. But trying to be presupposes that being isn't good enough. It is the negation of being in the belief that not being is somehow better. For example, if I say, "I am trying to be a better runner" this means that who I am is not good enough. But this is based on the assumption that I know who I am. And as we shall see shortly, most of us don't, holding instead a grossly inaccurate approximation of who we are. In other words, we think we know who we are when we really don't, the result of which is that in trying not to be who we think we are, we end up trying not to be who we are not. All of this may sound confusing, but perhaps the following analogy will help your understanding.

If I want to get to Chicago and I am in New York, it makes sense to drive west in order to get there. If I want to get to Chicago and think I'm in New York when I'm really in San Francisco, driving west will appear to make sense, but doing so will put me at the bottom of the Pacific Ocean. The upshot here is, if I want to get to Chicago, it is important to know who I am—in this particular case, a person in San Francisco, not a person in New York.

## Knowing Means Feeling

*You can't do what you want if you don't know what you're doing.*

-Moshe Feldenkrais

Dr. Feldenkrais is often quoted as saying, "You can't do what you want if you don't know what you're doing," which is really another way of saying, "You can't do what you want if you don't sense what you're doing." This is because knowing and sensing are actually one and the same phenomenon. Thus, the more you sense yourself, the more you know yourself. Conversely, the less you sense yourself, the less you know yourself. And the less you know yourself, the more you're like the person in San Francisco who tries to get to Chicago by driving West.

We can shorten all of this by simply saying, if you don't sense what you're doing then you are busy not being, rather than being yourself. And when you're busy not being rather than being, you can't do what you want.

If you understand this principle, then you will understand that the key to running with more power, is not to try to run like an Olympian, but rather to run like yourself. And the funny thing is, the more you run like yourself rather than trying to run like an Olympian, the more you will actually run like an Olympian (Yes, you read the last sentence correctly).

It's really that simple. Yet at the same time, it is difficult. We have spent so many years taking the hard way that we often know no other way. Making life difficult has become a habit.

## Common Non-sense

To run like yourself you have to know how you are actually running. And to discover how you are running, you have to sense and feel what you are doing when you run. Unfortunately, we live in a culture whose version of common sense encourages us to block out our senses. Our senses are in this manner, becoming non-senses. From the standpoint of improving and learning, it makes no sense—or perhaps more aptly put, non-sense—to mute your sense-abilities when doing so decreases power, speed, coordination and agility while dramatically increasing your chances of hurting yourself.

As stated in the previous two chapters, improving your sense-ability leads to reducing internal conflict, thereby increasing your control over the 630 muscles in your body. What's more, if you consider that muting your sense-ability simultaneous decreases your ability to know what is good for you and what isn't, then doing so also increases your reliance on others to tell you what is good for you. And if you are relying on others to decide what is good for you, then you are giving up your responsibility—that is, response-ability. When you sense less, in other words, you not only give up control over your own body, but your ability to respond appropriately to your own desires and needs. Sensing less you become less response-able.

Because sensing and feeling is inextricably tied to emotions, suppressing feelings can have similar effects on both your sense-ability and response-ability. Emotions, as we will see in Chapter 9 ("Who Turned Up the Gravity?"), play a pivotal role in movement. When you try to not be sad, angry or in pain by suppressing your feelings of sadness, anger or pain, you are effectively stifling both your movement possibilities and response-ability in one fell swoop. Of course doing so may be helpful in temporarily allowing you to fit in better (read, not show "negative" emotions), deal with physical trauma or simply make it through your workday, but habitual not being—that is, habitual suppressing of your sensing and feeling—comes at a cost.

Even without the use of drugs, many of us have already become habituated not to feel and therefore not to know ourselves. And we have spent so much time not feeling that we have actually lost much of the sensation in our own bodies. I experienced this first-hand after years of forcing myself to do things that I didn't like to do, such as continue running. And as my sense-ability decreased so did my coordination, power and speed. The frightening part about all of this was that I had become so accustomed to being numb that I unconsciously regarded my anaesthetized way of living as normal (even though I consciously felt miserable).

Once again, I am not alone.

A culture which places a premium on hurrying about, enduring discomfort at all costs and thereby "getting it done" is a culture which anaesthetizes its inhabitants. Not only have many physical ailments such as knee, back, neck and shoulder problems become the norm, but so have grim faces, forced smiles and perfunctory greetings. We as an entire culture have become so accustomed to not feeling, not knowing and not being, that these abnormal ways of living are now regarded as normal.

## ~~What's~~ Who's Stopping You?

> *I have taught many children and teenagers who were caught up in the*
> *belief that their self-worth depended on how well they performed at*
> *tennis and other skills.... Children who have been taught to measure*
> *themselves in this way often become adults driven by a compulsion*
> *to succeed which overshadows all else. The tragedy of this belief is not*
> *that they will fail to find the success they seek, but that they will not*
> *discover the love or even the self-respect they were led to believe will*
> *come with it.*
>
> -W. Timothy Gallwey

Trying to be and the consequent loss of sense-ability is, in short, a difficult way to live—or perhaps more aptly put, not quite live—because it means engaging in an internal battle. Trying to be something that I'm not, which is equivalent to trying not to feel who I am, is essentially like a game of football where I am playing defense against myself. This means that I am diverting a great deal of energy toward defeating myself the way the defense attempts to defeat the opposing offense. At the same time, I am trying my hardest to score a touchdown, meaning, I am trying to succeed. Trying to be thus translates to all of the work it takes to both score a touchdown and at the same time stop myself from scoring a touchdown. It requires the work of running an offense, and at the same time, running a defense that is trying to defeat the offense.

What do you think the outcome is? Watch a professional football game some time and you will see tempers flaring, bodies colliding, voices straining and nerves on edge. This is how many of us are unwittingly not quite living our lives. The conflicts and collisions may be internal and therefore remain somewhat hidden, but their evidence is betrayed by a host of physical and emotional disorders such as headaches, backaches, arthritis, insomnia, fibromyalgia and depression to name a few.

Many see such problems as an inevitable part of living in our fast-paced world. Many ailments are even considered to be part and parcel of the mysterious phenomenon medical experts call, "aging." Yet, if a culture drives people toward such suffering, what does it say about that culture?

For those of you who suffer, consider that on some level, dysfunction in a dysfunctional society (like ours) could be normal—even if specialists want to give you a drug for it. In a culture of common non-sense, in other words, dysfunction is like a big flashing billboard on the freeway of life saying, "Look here! There is another way!"

# Trying Harder Didn't Work.

*If trying hard didn't work, trying harder is doing more of what didn't work.*

-Charles Eisenstein

Trying to be, which is really just another way of saying, trying harder, normally translates to doing more of what I was doing before. So if like most people I am already playing defense on myself, trying harder means revving up the offense and defense at the same time. It is like stepping harder on the gas pedal when my engine is already overheating. Looking at it this way, the harder I try, the smaller my returns per measure of effort.

This is why for most people, there is an element of strain that accompanies an increase in effort. Strain can be read as an excessive amount of muscle contraction that not only contributes nothing to moving me forward, but actually contributes something to slowing me down by pulling me in undesired directions. Those directions could be down, up, sideways, and even backward. This means that for everyone including Olympic runners, trying harder actually results in more effort pulling in the wrong directions.

The difficulties don't end there because as I mentioned earlier, misdirected force does not simply disappear. Some of it inevitably ends up getting stuck in your joints, causing excessive compression, torsion and/or shearing stress (shearing force is what causes a coffee mug to slide off the kitchen table during an earthquake)—one reason why people who run with less power and ease also tend to get injured more easily.

In sharp contrast to trying to be, being remains the deepest part of us that only fully emerges after we remove all of the superimposed ideas that had been stacked on top. Instead of remaining shackled by thoughts about who we should be—often leading us to try to be who we are not—being allows us to come to our senses and draw forth what simply is. No longer playing defense on our self, something new then begins to flow through our body and mind.

The Bagua and Taichi masters refer to this flow as qi (sometimes written as, "chi"). They spend years unblocking and channeling it by tuning into different sensations in their bodies. This tuning in is the refinement of intention. As their intention becomes more and more refined, freeing them of unintended, parasitic contractions, their movement becomes more and more fluid and powerful.

From a biomechanical point of view, being allows force that was previously blocked or misdirected—resulting in less coordination and power—to travel unimpeded through your skeleton—resulting in more coordination and power. Being in other words, allows for a much smoother translation of force, thereby giving you far greater power and precision in movement. This smooth translation is how Bagua masters effortlessly toss people twice their weight through the air and how good runners propel themselves swiftly and smoothly to the finish line.

When you engage your sense-abilities you not only generate more power, but you stimulate the flow of everything from cerebral spinal fluid to oxygen, blood and lymph and other bodily liquids, gases and solids. Like unblocking a dam inside your own body, muscles that were previously tense, begin to release themselves and their constriction on all the vessels, tissues and organs beneath them, thereby freeing the nutrients and waste materials that were previously trapped within each to be easily transported.

In addition to increasing the flow of liquids, gases and solids, being changes the flow of electrochemicals through your nervous system. By letting go of parasitic contractions you sidestep the old well-worn neural pathways associated with constriction in order to generate new neural pathways—those associated with freedom of movement. Loosening the muscular straightjacket actually frees up your nervous system to create new, more sense-able pathways, such as those that awaken dormant muscles and tendons to direct force to where you want it to go.

When you begin to understand that being nurtures the flow of everything from mechanical force to blood, lymph and electrochemicals, you can more easily see that being is simply life itself coursing through your entire body. Thus, the more you are being, the more you embody life. Conversely, the less you are being—or in other words, the more you are trying to be, the more you hinder the flow of life.

## Running vs. Shuffling

As a final note on being, I recommend you tune into your level of pleasure every time you go for a run. If you begin noticing a consistent lack of enthusiasm, it means that part of you does not want to be running. And, as elucidated in Chapter 5 ("Intention"), the internal conflict will play out as parasitic contractions in some parts of yourself and a simultaneous collapse in others. The most obvious example of such conflict is when you see people shuffling through their daily "run." Shuffling is not running. Only running is running and it is important not to confuse the two. The more you shuffle and call it running, the more you not only habituate your body to moving in highly limited ranges of motion, but convince your mind into accepting this (mis)representation as running. By conflating shuffling and running, in other words, you are not only teaching yourself to move with restriction, but allowing a half-hearted imitation of running to stand for the real thing. Furthermore, the internal conflict and consequent increase in strain means that you are unconsciously linking the idea of running with struggle and displeasure, rather than freedom and pleasure.

If you set out to run and end up shuffling for a good portion of the time then I recommend calling what you have done a "shuffle" instead of a "run." It is important to have an accurate label and at the same time let go of any judgment you might have on that label because, as with anything else, shuffling is neither intrinsically good nor bad as long as you are aware that you are doing it. If done with awareness and clear intention, shuffling can even be a tool to improve your running, which is why I have devoted Lessons 18 and 19 to exploring the action.

By making a clear distinction between running and shuffling, you are clarifying your intention so that when your intention is to run, you really do run, even if only for half a block. Conversely, when you need to stop and rest, you won't find yourself shuffling out of a compulsion to keep working even though your body is telling your to do otherwise. By keeping your intention clear you will be fully invested in running when you are running and fully resting when you are resting. Meanwhile, you will be stepping away from the conflicted netherworld of half-running, half-resting or otherwise going through the motions. As a result, not only will your running stand a better chance of improving, but you will become more in tune with your own body, allowing it to rest when it truly wants to rest and exert itself when it truly wants to exert itself. Along with this, you will get far more enjoyment out of the process of either shuffling or running because you will be more aware of what you are really doing, which will in turn allow you to more accurately do what you really want to do. Once again, we come back to Dr. Feldenkrais' insightful statement, "you can't do what you want if you don't know what you're doing."

The next time you notice yourself shuffling when your intention was to run, take pause. Perhaps you are simply too tired to continue running. Perhaps shuffling has become a habit and you've lost touch with the joy of running. In either case I recommend you stop and walk rather than shuffle. Otherwise, by shuffling without intending to shuffle, you are actually showing your nervous system how not to run, and more importantly, you are habituating yourself to not being. This is why running enthusiastically for 100 meters and then stopping is far more beneficial to learning and improving than shuffling for 10 miles when you'd rather be doing something else.

Finally, if you are having difficulty getting motivated to run, I recommend you not force yourself. Millions of people around the world do not run and are perfectly happy, healthy and in shape. If it calls to you, try the experiment in Chapter 15 ("Compulsion") entitled, "Running for the Pleasure of It," or read the section that follows called, "Rediscovering Your Own (Ever-Changing) Pace," which describes possibilities for being more playful and in tune with your body and mind.

# Part II: Practical Matters

# Chapter 8

# Imitation: Why Trying to Run Like an Olympian Keeps You From Running Like an Olympian

> *If you stop 100 people at random and ask them to evaluate their driving ability, every single one will say, 'above average.' It is a scientific fact that all drivers, including those who are going the wrong way on interstate highways, believe they are above average. Not me, of course. I am currently ranked fourth among the top drivers in world history, between Mario Andretti and Spartacus.*
>
> -Dave Barry

Several summers ago I returned to Tianjin after spending an entire fall, winter and spring training rigorously on my own. It had been almost a year since I had seen the masters so I had a lot to show them. Eager to impress, I arrived early to greet Master Xueyi Li on the first day of training. A diminutive man lacking the girth and bravado of Master Ge, Master Li nonetheless carried an air of quiet self-assurance. Judging by his size and reticence, you wouldn't suspect that he had defeated high-level challengers from all over the city. Yet, once you saw him in action, or perhaps more accurately, lost sight of him in action, you knew you were in the hands of someone special. Master Li had a special knack of disappearing when going over two-person drills. One moment he was in front of you, and the next, he was behind you or at your flank. Meanwhile, his iron hands always came from nowhere, usually stopping half-an-inch from your face or some vital point on your body.

"Show me the first form," Master Li commanded in his usual quiet, but stern manner.

I began. Within seconds I heard him muttering something below his breath. Then a clear, "Stop." Master Li looked vaguely disinterested, as if he had better things to do. I hesitated.

"Stop," he repeated, sensing my desire to continue. "Show me the second form."

Ten seconds into the second form and again, unintelligible muttering. "Stop," he said with a hint of irritation. Master Li was apparently not nearly as impressed as I was.

"Third form," he said under his breath, as if ordering from a menu. He was looking at his watch.

I was hesitant to even begin. Obviously we should just call it off and go have breakfast. Ten seconds into the third form and I already knew what was coming.

This time there was no continuing. Master Li began to rattle off everything that I had been doing wrong. He pointed out places where he said I was rushing and not paying attention—place, in other words, where I lacked awareness. Quite a lot of "wrongness" considering my performance lasted a total of thirty seconds. I meanwhile stood in disbelief, feeling more than a little defiant knowing that it couldn't be as bad as he made it out to be.

Later, I when returned back to my dormitory, I decided to film myself going over the beginning of each form. Upon seeing myself in the viewfinder, I immediately knew that Master Li was right on all points. There were indeed, many flaws in my form, even if I had improved since the previous year. Obviously, I had not been not fully aware of how I had been moving. And until Master Li pointed out my mistakes, and they were corroborated by the camera, I was unaware that I was unaware.

## Know Thyself: The Three Cardinal Questions

In order to do what someone else is doing, you must first know what you yourself are doing. If you don't, then you'll be like the person in San Francisco, who tries to get to Chicago by driving west.

The knowing I'm referring to is actually not a static state, but a process of discovery and creation. If we pare it down to simple body mechanics, knowing yourself means discovering how you use the ground to generate force, how you translate this force through your body, and how new neural pathways are created in the entire process. If the ground is a springboard, your muscles are what direct the "spring" from the springboard through your body when you take off, and they are what direct the "spring" from your body back into the springboard when you land. Consequently, any lack of spring when you take off and any excessive "thud" when you land will be due to your muscles misdirecting the force.

All of this may sound complicated, but it really isn't if we view the concept of "know thyself" as a matter of understanding how to more efficiently direct our take-off and landing. It boils down to what I call, The Three Cardinal Questions:

1. How much effort does it take to move from one position to the next (and therefore, how can I minimize the effort)?
2. How solid is my connection with the floor?
3. Does it feel good?

Number one: How much effort does it take to move from one position to the next?

The less effort it takes to perform a given task—whether lifting a finger, or running the hundred meter dash—the less extraneous tension I will carry in my body and the lighter and more powerful I will feel.

Number two: How clear is my connection with the ground?

Whether I am sitting, standing, walking, or even lying down, my connection with the ground will reveal two important things: 1) How much extraneous tension I am carrying in my body, and 2) How much I'm collapsing in places where muscles are not fully supporting my structure.

The more tension I carry, the more that parts of me will unnecessarily pull away from the floor, making my contact with the floor less clear, precise and solid. This sort of tension could be reflected anywhere in my body—for example, in a tightness in my belly, a clenching in my jaw, a rising of my shoulders—and all of it serves to divert my center of gravity and pull me off balance and thereby affect how my feet or any other part (if I am sitting or lying down) make contact with the floor. Rather than feeling grounded into the floor, I will feel off-balance and out of kilter. Rather than pushing off with power and precision, my stepping will feel murky and unclear, perhaps akin to sloshing through mud.

While some muscles exhibit parasitic tension, others will likely remain chronically underused and relatively dormant. This further exacerbates the problem because the dormant muscles are not being used to do what they are designed for—namely, counterbalancing muscles that pull a particular joint in the opposite direction. The predictable result is further imbalance and less precision in how I make contact with the floor. Parts of my feet, for example, may collapse into the floor—the extreme example being fallen arches. And as we saw in Chapter 5 ("Intention") a collapse in any part of my body will affect the way that I use my entire body.

Number three: Does it feel good?

Pleasure and pain are the two most potent forces that guide movement and behavior. If it doesn't feel good then it probably isn't good for me. By finding ways to feel good, I actually transform my ways of moving and therefore, my ways of being in the world. One way to look at it is that the fastest, most powerful ways to run are also the most pleasurable ways to run.

# Distinctions

What asking the Three Cardinal Questions brings to light is who you are beneath the (superimposed) parasitic contractions. By wondering, in other words, you begin to shed unnecessary holdings associated with trying to be. This means as you ask, you shall be given—in this case a whole new world of distinction, discovery and transformation.

Making distinctions is in and of itself transformational because the human nervous system is actually wired with feedback loops in such a way that new neural pathways are created every time you discover with greater precision what it is that you are doing. These new pathways then become part of a new way of directing your muscles and therefore a new way of moving. And since movement is all that defines human behavior and expression, we can accurately say that making such distinctions results in a new way of being. In the process of making distinctions and thereby knowing yourself you are actually transforming yourself without trying to transform yourself.

From a practical standpoint, making distinctions results in greater precision in movement which can fundamentally improve the mechanics of your stride. To test the veracity of the last sentence, get ready to do Lesson 12 ("Mobilizing Your Ribcage"). If you explore the lesson slowly and attentively, you will actually improve your mechanical efficiency because you will be making the distinction between your unconscious habit of having your foot on the brakes so to speak, and the new conscious act of taking it off. Making the distinction is in and of itself what takes your foot off the brakes and therefore what allows you to generate more power, since effort that was previously devoted to slowing you down can now be used to speed you up.

Not surprisingly, Bagua masters are champions of making distinctions. To make finer distinctions, they break movements down into smaller pieces, slow down, and pay very close attention to what they are sensing and feeling. To stop slowing themselves down unintentionally, they first do it intentionally.

Making distinctions is in fact, how all humans sift out parasitic muscle tension and consequently gain more control and thus, more precision, power and coordination. Without the ability to make distinctions, we would have no possibility of improving the precision, power and coordination with which we move. In fact, we would have no precision, power and coordination at all.

Each time you make a new distinction, new neural pathways get stored in your brain. The more distinctions you make, the more neural pathways that get stored until at some point both your perception and movement will be noticeably different. To see an obvious example of this, watch an infant as she rolls around on the floor exploring movement. Though her explorations may appear random, what she is doing is making distinctions and thereby adding precision, coordination and control to her movement. From a neurological perspective, her persistent exploration is akin to tending to an apple tree. Each time she explores, she "sprouts" new branches in the form of neural pathways while simultaneously "pruning" and "weeding out" older, unused ones. The constant sprouting, pruning and weeding out produces an ever more intricate pattern in her brain. Over time, her perception and movement will become more and more refined. Initially only able to crawl, she will eventually bear the fruits of standing and walking.

What most distinguishes Olympians from most people is how much relative sprouting, pruning and weeding out they have done. What distinguishes them, in other words, is their ability to make finer distinctions and thereby control with more precision their 630-some-odd muscles. This edge in control allows them to run with much greater efficiency so that they waste far less energy per stride. Therefore, more energy goes toward propelling them forward, meaning that for every measure of effort they use, they get far greater returns.

Another way to look at distinctions is through the analogy of a racecar. An Olympic runner is like a racecar whose engine has been finely tuned, wheels aligned to the tiniest fraction of an inch and indeed, all the proper adjustments painstakingly made such that it runs at the highest level of efficiency. That very same car would run very differently if, however, had it been mistreated, in which case it wouldn't matter what kind of fuel you added, or how hard you stepped on the pedal. Nothing short of a major overhaul would get the latter running in peak condition.

When you consider that all bodies have the potential to run with higher—and often much higher—efficiency you begin to realize that how you tune yourself is absolutely vital to how well you run and how good you feel when you're in motion. To return to the racecar analogy, you are the mechanic for your own body, and by learning to make new distinctions you begin the process of fine-tuning yourself. If, on the other hand, you neglect the learning—as you do when you ignore your senses—no amount of effort, green leafy vegetables, or "high-octane" protein powder is going to improve your efficiency.

Perhaps now it is easier to understand what happens when we try to imitate great runners. Lacking their sense-ability, or in other words, their ability to make fine distinctions, we find ourselves unable to perform the way they do. Yet we behave as if increasing our effort will somehow achieve the desired result. Repetition of a flawed performance, however, does not lead to improvement—though it may lead to strain and injury.

## Know What You're Doing

If the biggest difference between the greatest and the great, the great and the good, the good and the average, is a matter of making finer distinctions through sensing, then it makes sense to sense more of what you are doing. As I mentioned in Chapter 7 ("To Be or Not To Be"), Dr. Feldenkrais is known for saying, "You can't do what you want if you don't know what you are doing." And you don't know what you are doing if you can't sense what you are doing. Knowing, in other words is sensing.

This means that short of improving your sense-ability, following the conventional route of performing rote exercises, lifting weights and following simple tips laid out by experts will have a minimal effect on improving the mechanics of your stride. The conventional route will help your stride, in other words, only if what you do can actually be felt while you are running. Surprisingly, following the conventional route may even be detrimental in certain cases since it tends to further ingrain self-destructive habits. As we saw in Chapter 5 ("Intention") such habits involve parasitic muscle contractions and stereotyped movement patterns that prevent you from running with more power and ease.

Lifting weights to build stronger muscles, for example, may be beneficial unless the added bulk it imparts to specific muscles goes toward pulling you even more off balance and more off course, thereby adding more stress to your ankles, knees, back and shoulders. Along with the stress to your joints, the added imbalance could ironically cause you to work even harder in order to keep yourself on course, thereby making running even more laborious. This is why people who lift weights are not necessarily more powerful and fluid in activities that don't involve a dumbbell. Surprisingly, many people in the gym haven't learned to sense and therefore use their bodies in a manner that allows for the force to go where they want it to go. And herein lies the key to improving your stride:  in order to use yourself powerfully, you must know what you are doing. And to know what you are doing, you must be able to make distinctions by sensing and feeling what you are doing. The more you can sense what you are doing, the more unified your intention and the greater your power.

So when you really take the time to sense more, you begin to tap into the vast reservoir of power and grace that great runners have been tapping into. By sensing more, your stride actually becomes more like that of an Olympian.

## Know Others (Including Their Anatomical Differences)

Human proportions vary considerably from continent to continent, region to region and race to race. In parts of Sub-Saharan Africa such as Kenya, for example, people exhibit a higher center of gravity because they have a shorter torso to leg ratio. The result is more curvature in their spine. In parts of East Asia such as China and Japan we see the opposite:  people have a lower center of gravity because they possess longer torsos relative to the length of their legs. The result is less curvature in their spine.

People's legs also come in different shapes and sizes depending on ancestry. The crural index measures the length of the tibia, or shinbone, relative to the femur, or thighbone. Scientists have discovered that people whose ancestors come from the same region tend to exhibit similar crural indexes—which is to say their legs are proportionally similar.

So what does all of this have to do with running?

The anatomical structure of humans by and large determines what kind of posture and patterns of movement best suit them. Someone with a higher center of mass and higher crural index may run more efficiently, for example, using a style that doesn't suit someone with a lower center of mass. It may be more efficient for Kenyans to run by leaning a little forward. But does this mean that it is just as efficient for Norwegians or Japanese to do the same? Someone with entirely different skeletal proportions might not be well suited to leaning forward any more than Catherine Ndereba or any of the other great Kenyan runners might be suited to running very erect. Simply put, your body type will likely require a different style of running in order for you to run as smoothly and powerfully as someone with a different body type. By trying to imitate the Kenyans, you might actually be choosing a less efficient way to run and thereby slowing yourself down. In the process, you would also be missing out on discovering different ways of running that are more ideal for your particular structure.

Each person is pointing to the same part of their hips. Notice how the distance from the kneecap to the hip is different for each person.

Anatomical differences aside, there is the important issue of what we think someone is doing compared to what they are actually doing. Obviously if we want to accurately imitate what someone is doing, we must first accurately know what they are doing. On first glance, Catherine Ndereba and other great Kenyan runners may appear to be leaning forward as they come down the homestretch. Yet are they really leaning forward or is the pronounced curvature in their spine creating the illusion that they are leaning forward? And if they truly are leaning, from which joint(s) do they lean? If you consider that it's possible to lean from your ankles, hips, any of the 24 vertebrae in your spine, or any combination of the abovementioned, then you can see how the prospect of imitating someone is ripe with pitfalls.

Finally, even if we have figured out precisely what someone else is doing, being able to do it ourselves is often much harder than it looks. For example, the vast majority of people who are instructed to lean will very rarely do it in the same manner as someone like Catherine Ndereba (assuming she herself leans while running). Instead, they will lean by utilizing all of their particular senso-rimotor habits rather than the habits of a great Kenyan runner. It's not for a lack of effort that they are unable to accurately carry out the task, but that everybody's sensorimotor habits arise from their own individual sense-abilities. Thus, if you don't have the sense-abilities of a great Kenyan runner, you won't be able to move like a great Kenyan runner, no matter how hard you try. When attempting to lean forward like the Kenyans, some people will consequently collapse their chest forward, forcing them to crane their neck back, while others will hunch their back causing other distortions in the spine. Such inaccurate imitations will naturally produce completely different results, none of which is likely to achieve the desired gain in power.

Obviously, the problem here is not that we don't know how to lean forward, but that we don't really know how to do it in the manner of a Catherine Ndereba. In other words, if I lean forward, but lack the requisite sense-ability of a Kenyan track star, I will do it in my particular way—that is, using my particular movement habits—which is quite different from the way the Kenyan track star does it. And believe it or not, something so simple as leaning forward has as many variations as there are people on the planet.*

## Posture: "Oops, I swallowed a yardstick!"

Whether or not any of us tries to lean the way a Kenyan track star appears to be leaning, many people agree that it's important run with a "straight" back. Many people also believe that "straightness," or what is deemed, "good posture"—whether for sitting, standing or running—must be imposed on an otherwise crooked body. This being the case, where does the crookedness come from?

Our collective obsession with posture is itself revealing to how the dominant culture views life. Posture comes from the Latin word, *positura*, meaning station or position, which presupposes a static and therefore unchanging state. Yet in order to maintain our "station or position," we must ignore our senses since paying attention to them, as we shall see, would mean constantly changing our station or position. And unfortunately, if we ignore our senses, we must rely on outside sources to define what is good and what is bad.

Obviously, life is not static as the word posture would lead us to believe. Rather, it is perpetually in flux and thus, perpetually asking us to adapt our movement to suit the task at hand, be it running, getting out of a chair, or simply standing in line at the check-out counter. And whereas stasis insinuates predictability and some level of confinement, adaptability is itself, freedom.

For those of us with postural issues we are in effect, experiencing confinement created by our habits. To break out of the prison, it won't help to force

---

* In their bestselling book, *ChiRunning*, Danny and Katherine Dreyer have developed some creative and useful exercises that help you lean forward without collapsing your spine.

"good" posture on ourselves. In fact, we actually experience the opposite of freedom when we attempt to "sit up straight," "stand tall," or otherwise walk around with a "straight" back. We intuitively know something isn't right because trying to be "straight" usually doesn't feel so good. In fact after very a short time—and we can normally only hold it for a matter of seconds—it feels tiresome and uncomfortable. Sit up straighter right now and see how long you end up staying there. If you're like me, and most people I know, it will be ten seconds or less before a distraction will lead you back to your habitual posture.

The reason forcing changes in posture doesn't feel good is because you are attempting to impose something new on top of something else that doesn't just magically disappear. You end up with two minds jockeying for position in one body, or to use an earlier analogy, you end up with offense and defense playing against each other. Because the old habitual patterns are still there, in other words, forcing something on top of it is a form of suppression. You can literally feel the internal struggle through increased effort.

We can usually sense when people around us are trying to imitate good posture simply because they look stiff and uncomfortable. In trying to be straight, they look like they are trying to fit themselves into a mold—perhaps a bit like soldiers who are standing at attention. Dr. Feldenkrais himself commented on how we are all familiar with people among us who have swallowed a yardstick. We are familiar because we ourselves do it from time to time when we are trying to impress others.

## Freedom

> *Life! Life!*
> *Tell it like it is.*
> *You don't have to die before you live!*
>
> -Sly & the Family Stone

Ideally, the human body is not static like the frozen spine of a drill sergeant standing at attention, but active like that of a Olympic runner who can at one moment bound powerfully down the track, and the next moment, gracefully bend down to tie her shoe. Because the bounding and bending require very different uses of her spine and indeed her entire body from head to toe, the stasis implicit in the word, posture, is misleading.

Realizing this, Dr. Feldenkrais coined a more adaptive term for how we could be carrying ourselves as we go through life. *Acture*, which comes from the Latin root, *actus*, meaning "a doing," insinuates action and change. Since Dr. Feldenkrais believed that the way we carry ourselves could become more and more of an active process, keeping ourselves static actually prevents us from moving well.*

For Dr. Feldenkrais, the concept of acture is meant, not only to insinuate action, but moreover actions we most often carry out. This means that how I normally carry myself is simply an outward manifestation of the movement patterns I use most often. So if I spend eight hours a day hunched over a desk and craning my chin forward in order to see my computer screen, the hunching and craning movement patterns may eventually become dominant—even when I am not at my desk. Conversely, the more my daily repertoire reflects a sense-able adaptation to everyday tasks, the more efficient, graceful and powerful my acture becomes.

All of this is to say that good acture (or, if you prefer, "good posture"), is the result of having greater sense-ability in everyday life. Good acture, in other words, comes naturally through tuning into my senses, rather than tuning out of them through force and willpower. If my daily activities include training in a way that allows me to discover more powerful, coordinated and graceful ways to carry my body down the track, then the accrued movement patterns will make me taller, more powerful and coordinated even when I'm not training. You'll notice for example, how effortlessly tall and erect Olympic track athletes stand and walk. They aren't trying to be tall, they simply are tall as a result of their movement habits. Conversely, the more I employ movement patterns that are not linked with greater sense-ability, and consequently not linked to more power, coordination and fluidity, the heavier, less coordinated and possibly shorter I will feel.** I cannot simply imbibe power, coordination and fluidity and thus magically absorb good acture. Good acture can only come through one avenue: sensing more.

Here again, we return to the fact that in order to successfully imitate (in this case "good" acture), I need to sense and feel and therefore know what's happening inside myself. I cannot artificially impose good acture on myself and expect to look, feel and move like the people I am trying to imitate. To do so is to look for a shortcut that doesn't exist. The potent acture that Olympians carry is a natural result of finely tuning the racecar so to speak. Attempting to copy their potent acture by leaning forward or forcing myself to stand tall, on the other hand, is like stepping on the gas, hoping that sheer willpower and force will produce a

---

* It is important to note that everybody does, in fact, adapt to some degree to the task at hand. The issue Feldenkrais makes, however, is that few of us adapt to a high degree. Thus, we may continue to keep our backs straight even when it's not appropriate (such as when bending down to tie our shoelaces).

** I believe that getting shorter as we age is not simply a function of bone loss, but concomitant with the ways that we habitually carry ourselves. The people who grow shorter at a faster rate are likely those who carry faulty acture. It's encouraging to note here that it is actually possible to stand taller with age if you continue to improve your sense-ability and thereby improve you're acture. During my Feldenkrais training, I was astonished to discover myself going through a "growth spurt" where I literally grew taller. Even though the objective gain in height was minimal—probably a fraction of an inch over four years—the subjective feeling made me feel ten feet tall. The feeling of standing tall, for the first time in my life, in other words, made me feel like a whole new person—more empowered than I had felt in decades.

superior performance. Good acture, in other words, does not cause my movement repertoire to suddenly expand. Rather, it is a result of the movement repertoire that already exists. Simply standing "straighter" or leaning forward, then does not automatically cause me to have the movement repertoire and therefore the powerful stride of the great Kenyan runners. Increasing my sense-ability and thereby adding movement patterns to my repertoire, however, does allow me to run with more power and does affect my acture in a positive way.

## Are You Saying Imitation is Bad?

Imitation itself is not the trap per se. Rather, it is the assumption that 1) we know ourselves; 2) we know others.

Does this mean we should never imitate somebody else?

No. What it means is that if it's to be of benefit to us, we need to pay attention to how imitating someone's movement feels in our own bodies. If we want to be more accurate in imitating movement patterns, we need to start discovering first of all, what it is we are actually doing in our own bodies. Then and only then, will we be able to accurately discover what it is that other people are doing in theirs.

The pitfall here is that we normally possess an idea of what we are doing that bears little resemblance to what it is we are actually doing. The same goes for watching other people. We think we know what they are doing, when in fact, all we possess is a crude approximation—often wrought with illusion—of their way of moving. Whether or not we are accurate in our ideas of ourselves or in approximating others is left to us to discern through meticulous exploration and frequently asking the Three Cardinal Questions.

As a final note to this chapter, you'll notice that not all world-class runners lean forward when they run. And not all of them run as tall and erect as someone like the great 400 meter champion, Michael Johnson. In fact most do neither for one very good reason: it doesn't feel good to them. This is not to say trying to imitate Catherine Ndereba's forward alignment or Michael Johnson's straight up and down carriage is wrong, but rather that imitating any particular style is not a necessary key to running more efficiently.

To get a good idea of how the position of your spine—leaning or not—affects how much power you have going up stairs and up hills, go to Lesson 10 ("Standing Tall Without Trying to Stand Tall").

# Chapter 9

# Who Turned Up the Gravity?

*Gravity is, if you will, the universe's nearest approximation to what theologians might call an immanent deity: namely, a God that is universal, ubiquitous, law-giving, and all powerful.*

-Thomas Hanna

Life is anything but static. Yet modern culture leads us to believe that it is, causing us to do all we can to resist change and cling to our habits. Unfortunately, our habits don't always serve us well.

Perhaps the only thing that remains static is gravity. The earth exerts a constant pull, yet we perceive the constancy as change. We describe this change with words like "light" or "heavy," "powerful" or "weak," "fluid" or "jerky," "grounded" or "ungrounded." Though we may often feel like someone is turning the gravity dial up or down, it is not gravity that is changing, but rather our relationship with it.

Why would our relationship with gravity continue to change?

Because to be alive is to move, and to move requires that you find a way to maintain your balance. Simply lifting your leg requires a whole series of adjustments in order to stabilize certain joints and keep you from falling on your face. In order for some part of you to move, other parts have to provide a stable foundation for that movement. Moving one part of your body, in other words, is not really moving just that one part. It is moving that part in concert with the entire rest of your body—or simply put, it is your whole body moving at once, though it may appear as if only one part is in motion. One way to look at it is like this: if I reach forward with my foot, is it my foot that is reaching forward, or my body that is reaching backward with respect to my foot?

This is why when running one leg goes backward as the other goes forward. This is also why the faster you run, the more you pump your arms. As we saw earlier, it isn't just the legs that are moving. Everything above your waist can be used to support or even initiate what is happening below your waist. Imagine running with your arms bound to your sides by rope and you will immediately have a sense of how important the arms are for maintaining balance and increasing power.

## Gravity, Effort and the Three Cardinal Questions

Answering the Three Cardinal Questions is a way to measure our relationship with gravity. The amount of effort we need to exert in order to do anything describes the degree to which gravity has become our friend or our enemy. Generally speaking, the less refined our sense-ability, the less efficiently we move.* And the less efficiently we move, the heavier we feel and therefore the more effort we need to exert in order to do whatever it is we want to do. Efficiency can be reflected in any aspect of living, from lifting your hand to sprinting down the street. It can even be reflected in the way you breathe and sleep. For example, do you ever feel like you can't get enough air, maybe even to the degree that it feels like someone is pressing on your chest? Any difficulty in breathing means that you are not only working harder in order to do what should come naturally, but getting less oxygen in the process. In many cases, unintentional constriction in your chest and abdomen literally holds your breath in. The question you might then ask is, "Who is holding my breath?"

Everything in life can be linked to effort. When we say things like "I'm walking on clouds," "She's got the weight of the world on her shoulders," or "He sucked the air out of the room," we are in a sense referring to the amount of effort we need to exert in order to accomplish a particular task—even if that task is as basic as breathing. In fact, each emotion and feeling is attached to a corresponding acture, or in other words, a particular neuromuscular pattern which affects your entire body. And each neuromuscular pattern in turn determines how much effort you are exerting. When you're walking on clouds, you will experience very little effort in each step. In contrast, when you've got the weight of the world on your shoulders, or somebody has sucked the air out of the room, your entire body will feel heavy and each step or breath you take will feel laborious.

All of this is to say that we literally make ourselves feel lighter or heavier, depending on what emotions are coursing through us from moment to moment. This is why coaches, sportscasters and athletes talk so much about momentum and morale changes in the heat of the battle. When the momentum shifts in

---

* Of course to be efficient, your sense-abilities must relate on some level to the activity at hand. While a concert pianist will have highly developed sense-abilities for the playing the piano, such sense-abilities will probably not translate easily to running or swimming powerfully. Likewise, while Olympic runners possess sense-abilities that relate to efficient propulsion on land, they probably won't help much for swimming or playing the piano.

a football game, it means that one team has suddenly lost its emotional edge, which in turn corresponds to a change in the athletes' acture. Players who have lost their morale will suddenly feel more tired and their acture will reflect this. Unless they can change their emotional state, they will be stuck in acture and therefore, movement patterns that are less efficient and more effortful.*

## Emotions and Acture

Clenching your jaws and holding your breath are so common in modern society that you might consider them a part of normal behavior. Indeed, they are so normal for most of us as to go unnoticed. Watch anybody driving in traffic, or trying to complete a task in the office, or chopping vegetables, and these telltale signs of tension will invariably appear.

In my classes, students will occasionally start giggling and almost always apologize for doing so. My response is to encourage them to laugh more. In fact, I encourage some amount of laughter in my classes because nobody I've ever met can both laugh and hold their breath or clench their jaw at the same time. Interestingly, as soon as the jaw begins to release and the chest begins to fill with air, other parasitic patterns begin to disappear: the shoulders start to let go, the back gains more flexibility, the ribcage becomes more supple.

It is ironic that students will apologize for laughing, but not for frowning, or looking apathetic, which is far more common in our culture. Part of it may be that many people are by and large unaware of the angry, fearful, anxious, apathetic and annoyed expressions they carry out into the world. And they are unaware that any change in their emotional state is reflected not only in their face, but in their acture and ways of moving. For some individuals, such expressions may have become ingrained sensorimotor (and therefore, emotional) habits, which will at some point carve distinct "frowning" lines into their faces, if they haven't been carved in already.

This is, of course, not to say that we should always be happy and smiling. If we were to try to accomplish happiness say, through "positive thinking," we would be like the person who "swallows a yardstick" in order to stand straighter. We would be, in other words, simply imposing an external "correctness" on our-

---

* Players who have lost their morale will appear to have given up, and during a game this is considered to be bad. I consider giving up to be neither intrinsically bad nor good, but simply a necessary part of learning. Great innovations and improvements often come after we've engaged in an intensive period of work and "given up" to rest for a while. We often hear stories of people coming up with new ideas while relaxing in the bathtub or somewhere else. Richard Feynman, for example, first got the idea for what was to become his Nobel Prize-winning thesis while sitting in the university dining hall: "…he was eating in the student cafeteria when someone tossed a dinner plate into the air—a Cornell cafeteria plate with the university seal imprinted on one rim—and in the instant of its flight he experienced what he long afterward considered an epiphany. As the plate spun, it wobbled. Because of the insignia he could see that the spin and the wobble were not quite in synchrony. Yet just in that instant it seemed to him—or was it his physicist's intuition?—that the two rotations were related. He had told himself he was going to play, so he tried to work out the problem on paper." -Richard Feynman

selves, hoping that the internal reality would magically disappear.

What I'm suggesting instead is we have the option of increasing our awareness without at the same time increasing self-judgment: that is, we have the option of wondering from time to time, which ways of perceiving and perhaps, reacting to the world have become habitual.

## Laughing and Frowning Involve Distinctly Different States of Acture

All of your movements are affected by what you are feeling, not only physically, but emotionally. This is because each separate feeling and emotion involves a different acture that encompass your entire musculature. Laughing, for example, involves your entire body in a neuromuscular pattern that is distinctly different from frowning. This is why it helps to be aware of so-called "negative emotions" when you're engaging in sports. Fear, anxiety, anger, boredom and resentment, for example, reveal themselves through different neuromuscular states that contribute to some muscles being overly tense and others overly flaccid.* This in turn can translate to choppier and less controlled movement, and in the case of running, a shorter and weaker stride. Of course, some athletes utilize anger to create more tension as a way of getting "psyched up."

## Turning Down Gravity

The relationship between acture, movement patterns and effort is why it can be so enlivening to improve your sense-abilities. Improved sense-abilities generally help to improve your relationship with gravity, making you feel lighter—as if Mother Nature just turned down the gravity dial.

The relationship described above is also one reason why Olympic coaches stress the importance of maintaining your form when you start to fatigue. Each minute change in form can do either one of two things: 1) pull you off balance, causing you to immediately become less efficient because you consequently need to devote more of your energy to simply staying in balance; or 2) make you more balanced, meaning more of your energy goes toward propelling you forward, rather than in some undesired direction.

The difficulty here is that when you get tired, it becomes more difficult to control your muscles and therefore more likely that you will begin to lose your form and thereby unwittingly increase your workload. To some degree, losing form is a natural part of muscle fatigue because when you start to tire, it is more difficult to control your movement. But this doesn't mean that your movement has to be totally out of control.

---

* I hesitate to label any emotion, "negative," because I believe that all emotions are intrinsic to being fully alive. When we view certain emotions as negative, we are more likely to impose other emotions on top, thereby suppressing the original. And just as trying to force "good posture" on ourselves doesn't make the old habits go away, trying to force "positive emotions" on ourselves simply suppresses what we are truly feeling.

When some people begin to tire their form really falls apart. I am quite familiar with this phenomenon because I used to clench my shoulders and swing my head wildly whenever I started getting tired. This created enormous stress on my body because it caused more energy to be diverted toward propelling me in the wrong direction, which forced me to spend even more energy to keep myself running in the right direction. Without realizing it, I had done the equivalent of plopping a sandbag on my shoulders—and I did it at a time when I was least able to deal with added stress.

So when your form falls apart, you are actually giving yourself more work. And this means that the more your form disintegrates, the more effort you need to exert to stay on track—and literally stay on the track, because parasitic muscle tension may be pulling you off the track.

Looking at it this way, effort is a measure of the quality of your stride. The more efficient you are, the more propulsion you get per measure of effort. Or, put more simply, higher efficiency means that you can travel the same distance and do so faster, while exerting less effort. Conversely, the less efficient your stride, the more proverbial sandbags you are carrying on your shoulders and therefore the more effort you need to expend.

This is not to say that great runners don't use effort. They exert a tremendous amount. But for each amount, they literally cover more ground because less of their work goes toward piling sandbags on their shoulders and more of it goes toward propelling their bodies forward. As a result, each individual stride will propel them much further than that of the average jogger. And this is why they look so light when they are running—as if they are floating on air.

To maintain to better form, even as you fatigue, it helps to practice tuning into specific points in your body from time to time. Then when you get tired or are pushing it down the homestretch, it will be much easier to focus on these points. For example, you could focus on keeping the back of your neck long, reaching for the sky with the center top of your head, or pushing off from particular metatarsals. Lesson 14 ("Water Jugs, Furniture and Other Things to Carry on Your Head") addresses the former two and many of the lessons from the "Throwing the Ball" series address pushing off from different parts of your foot. Whatever places you choose, every now and then practice bringing your attention to them while running.

# Chapter 10

# Following Instructions: Where Do My Knees Begin?

*A man and his son are in a serious car accident. The father is killed, and the son is rushed to the emergency room. Upon arrival, the attending doctor looks at the child and gasps, 'This child is my son!' Who is the doctor?*

*This is an insight puzzle. It's not like a math or a logic problem that can be worked out systematically with pencil and paper. The only way you can get the answer is if it comes to you suddenly in the blink of an eye. You need to make a leap beyond the automatic assumption that doctors are always men. They aren't always, of course. The doctor is the boy's mother!*

-Malcolm Gladwell

Over the years I have noticed two vital questions that few of us ask ourselves when being given "expert" advice:

Should I follow the advice?
How should I follow the advice?

Before following someone else's advice, it is a good idea to examine the foundation upon which the advice is based. This is because behind every instruction lies a series of assumptions of which even the advice-givers may be unaware. Look closely at any piece of writing from a physics textbook to The New York Times to this running book and you will find a world of assumptions. This isn't a bad thing. We need them in order to make sense of and thereby organize our world. You could say that assumptions are a way of simplifying the world into something more manageable. They allow us to make generalizations such as, "touching a hot stove hurts," or "getting enough sleep puts me in a better mood." And in this manner, assumptions form the basis of what we have already learned.

What we have learned in the past, however, is not always appropriate for the present. And this means that learning—which only takes place in the present—could be considered the active process of uncovering assumptions—specifically false ones.

Because assumptions are generally made on an unconscious level, it is difficult to notice them. The average person in the modern industrialized world, for example, assumes that the terrain on which she walks is completely flat and even. This is evident in her gait and explains why she is more likely to stumble when she meets an unexpected crack in the sidewalk as compared to someone who is used to navigating uneven terrain. The assumption itself is neither good nor bad but a natural part of the way the human nervous system adapts to its environment. And in this way assumptions may serve us, but only to the degree that the terrain never changes.

As humans, we all trip over literal and proverbial cracks in the sidewalk from time to time. Doing so affords us the opportunity to really start paying attention to the terrain. But as I mentioned earlier, paying attention requires slowing down—a difficult endeavor when you live in a world where everything is speeding up. Thus, we are caught in what appears to be a dilemma. To keep up with the world I have to speed up. But to learn from my mistakes I need to slow down. Which do I choose?

To slow down is in a sense to speed up because by taking my time, I gain all the clarity, accuracy and precision that come with learning. From a neuro-physiological standpoint, slowing down gives my nervous system the opportunity to absorb much more information, make distinctions and fine-tune my motor control so that when I choose to speed up again, my movement will be more precise and less hampered by parasitic muscle contractions. To re-visit an earlier analogy, if want to drive to Chicago and I live in San Francisco, heading west will not get me to my destination any faster, no matter how hard I step on the gas.

Another way to look at it is that by refusing to slow down I am liable to make the same mistakes over and over. For refusing to slow down is in many cases equivalent to refusing to pay attention. And to those of us who refuse to pay attention, our constant stumbling will remain a mystery. We will continue driving into the ocean and blame the car, not realizing that it's our lack of attentiveness that has brought us to where we are.

## How Should I Follow Instructions?

This is another way of saying, "What do the instructions really mean?" For example, what does it mean when someone says, "lift your knees higher"?*

These questions may appear to be silly because we think we understand simple instructions. The problem is very few instructions are as simple as they first appear. As I mentioned earlier, "lean forward when you run" is a very complex instruction requiring you to really understand body mechanics and differences between your body and the body of the person you're trying to imitate. In the end, this seemingly simple instruction turns out to be quite ambiguous. The common dictum among track coaches, "Lift your knees higher," is similarly rife with pitfalls.

From a conventional coaching perspective, lifting your knees higher means just that. So whenever coaches told me to do lift my knees, it's what I tried to do. What we didn't realize, however, is that as with leaning forward, there is an untold number of ways to lift your knees higher. Furthermore, none of us knew that the simple instruction, lift your knees higher contains three major assumptions: 1) that there is only one right way to lift your knees higher; 2) that I would be able to figure out how to do it that one right way; and 3) that by doing it that one right way I would actually become a better runner.

Try it now if you like: run down the hallway and lift your knees higher than you normally do. Is it relatively more or less effort to do? If it is more, how long do you think you could sustain that increased level of effort? Do you feel lighter or heavier? How do your back and neck feel? Take some time to really notice.

## Operator

Giving and following instructions is like giving and receiving messages in the children's game called "Operator." With several children sitting in a circle, the game begins when one child whispers a short message to the one next to her. The second child in turn passes the message on to the child next to him. The message goes around in the circle until it returns to the first child. Simple enough.

Yet the results reveal that passing a message is not so simple. In fact, the whole fun in the game is discovering how the message returns to the original sender and bears little or no resemblance to the original. The amusement, in other words, is in how the content gets to be totally and unintentionally revised. While each child has tried her best to pass on the original message, each has unwittingly changed it through her own interpretive skills.

Interpretation is not only limited to children playing a game, but it is part and parcel of all communication, including that between adults. This means that

---

* I heard this phrase over and over when I was a serious runner. The assumption here is that by lifting your knees higher you will run faster. Yet, if you watch films of Alberto Salazar who won three consecutive New York City Marathons back in the early 80s, or Michael Johnson, who dominated the 200 and 400 meter dash in two Olympiads, you will notice that neither lifts his knees as high as his competitors. Obviously, the assumption that lifting your knees higher makes you faster remains true only some of the time.

each of us, regardless of age, will interpret the same instructions in a different fashion. Each of us, in other words, will choose one among a countless number of ways to perform the instruction. Thus, even the simplest instructions will yield different results for different people.

So the question then becomes, how do you get an accurate interpretation?

The answer is you generally don't because you are interpreting the instructions through your ability to understand them. And this ability rests on the depth of your sense-ability. If you happen to already possess the requisite sense-ability that would allow you to move as the instructor intends, then you will get a fairly accurate interpretation. The problem is few of us possess the requisite sense-ability at the outset, and if we did, we probably wouldn't be looking for help to begin with.

This fact notwithstanding, you can still reap benefits from following (interpreting) instructions, if you view all learning as a process and take each new instruction as an experiment. In this case, what you are looking for is how each interpretation of each new instruction affects the way you feel. Pay attention to the process, in other words, and you will maximize your learning and improvement.*

And this brings us back to the Three Cardinal Questions. Here they are again:

How much effort does it take to move from one position to the next (and therefore, how can I minimize the effort)?

How solid is your connection with the ground?

Does it feel good?

As I elucidated earlier, asking the Three Cardinal Questions assures that you are staying in tune with your senses and therefore your mind, which makes you much more likely to become engrossed in the process rather than fixating on the end result. In this manner, asking the Three Cardinal Questions when interpreting any instructions not only prevents you from doing damage to yourself, but dramatically enhances your learning and your ability to feel pleasure.

In contrast, by fixating on "getting it done" or "getting results" and thereby not staying in process, you are not only more likely to get injured, but less likely to improve. What's more, performing in a rote way—which is what happens when you are not being mindful—you will have taken the fun out of learning.

---

* Note that the instructions contained in this book are designed to cut out as many variables as possible so as to make the interpretation easier. Learning occurs most rapidly when your mind only has to deal with one or two variables at once. Too many, and the mind gets overwhelmed. Mathematicians and scientists commonly use the principle of minimizing variables, knowing that having too many prevents them from making new discoveries. Athletes and martial artists do this in form of simple drills that get more complex as they master more skills. Watch a varsity basketball or soccer practice some time and you will get an idea of what it means to minimize variables.

Indeed, you will have taken the learning out of learning thereby turning your directed actions into a boring and possibly self-destructive chore.

## The Complexity of the Human Body

Another reason following even simple instructions is wrought with so many pitfalls has to do with the underlying assumption that people will follow them in a way that deepens their sense-abilities, thereby creating more efficient movement patterns. Those who are giving the instructions in other words unwittingly assume that by following their advice people will discover new ways of moving that reside outside of their habitual patterns. Recall that if you continue to use your old movement patterns, you won't improve in any fundamental way and what's more, you will end up practicing all of your habits. By practicing your habits, you won't in other words, learn. This works fine if like Catherine Ndereba, you already possess good running habits, but not so well if you don't (though even world-class runners can benefit from discovering new movement patterns). To go back to an earlier analogy, practicing habits is for most of us akin to fortifying our defense, or in other words, perfecting the art of self-sabotage.

Why it is so difficult to accurately follow instructions has to do with the complexity of the human body and mind. Though many instructions appear to be simple, each and every one invariably presents the nervous system with an overwhelming number of choices. How do you move some 630 muscles attached to over 200 bones and controlling roughly 230 joints vis-à-vis an ever-changing environment, in a way that corresponds to what your coach or author intended?

If you consider that in combination all of these bones, joints and muscles present a potential for movement which is virtually limitless, you can begin to understand why the human mind dwarfs even the most sophisticated supercomputer in its ability to integrate patterns. And you can also understand how easy it is to miss the mark.

## The Knee Bone's Connected to the Thigh Bone, the Thigh Bone's Connected to the…

Because your knee is connected to your shin, it is inextricably linked to the movement of your shin and everything below your shin—namely your foot and ankle. In addition, your knee is connected above to your thighbone, which is inextricably linked to the movement of the pelvis. Your pelvis itself acts like the Grand Central Station of bodily movement because it is the central nexus that links all the pieces together. Not only does your pelvis help to integrate the right and left sides of your body, but it connects the upper and lower half and front and back as well. If you were to break down the force vectors that travel through your pelvis with each movement you make, it would look like a massive circuit board with seemingly endless bundles of circuits going to every part of the body.

Looking at the body in this relativistic way, you can begin to see that when something goes up, something else has to go down. And when something goes forward, something else must go backward. Indeed, when something goes in one direction something else must go in another. Newtonian physics makes another appearance here. Look at the form of good runners and you will notice that when the right knee lifts, it doesn't do so in isolation. The entire body is moving relative to the knee: the left shoulder and arm simultaneously reach forward; the left hip extends backward, the right shoulder and arm pump backward. And here we run into a conundrum: is it the right knee going forward that causes the rest of the body to react and move in their particular ways, or is it the entire rest of the body that is driving the right knee forward? What is the cause and what is the effect?

By focusing our attention on the knees, my coaches and I unwittingly treated them as the cause. And by doing so, we neglected how the rest of my body played a role in my stride. Would it have been better to look at some other part of the body as the cause?

## Symbiosis vs. Cause and Effect

Rather than looking at movement in the conventional way—as independently moving parts—I believe it is much more instructive to see your body as a unified whole in which each part is inextricably linked with the entire rest of you—not only neurologically through sensing and feeling (as we saw in Chapter 8: "Imitation: Why Trying to Run Like an Olympian Keeps You From Running Like an Olympian"), but biomechanically through force vectors, gravity and the flow of life or qi.

Cause and effect, which is the conventional way of looking at how the universe works, harkens back to the reductionistic way of breaking the world down into discrete, independently moving parts. But what of the possibility that our "discrete parts" actually work symbiotically such that one movement is not strictly the cause of another? If this were the case, then we could begin to see how each muscle and bone plays a reciprocal role in how the entire rest of our body moves. From this perspective, the way I use my left shoulder could play a major role in how I move my right knee, and vice versa. Even the way I use my left big toe could have a significant impact on how I carry my head, and vice versa. Parts that are seemingly removed and distant from each other, in other words, are not so removed or distant when we begin to understand biomechanics as a symbiotic phenomenon.

Symbiosis is not a new concept. The Bagua precepts state that if the center moves, the extremities move, and if the extremities move, the center moves. Bagua could, in this manner, be seen as a search for unification, the practice of which is to unify movement within one's body, and thereby unify intention within one's mind.

Powerful running follows the same precepts even if running coaches and running books don't explicitly state this. Generally speaking, the more powerful and graceful a movement feels, the more you are using yourself as a unified whole in which the "parts" work cooperatively. The less powerful and graceful you feel, the more likely you are moving like a machine whose parts are not cooperating.

All of the lessons in Appendix II address symbiosis. Try any one of them now to have an embodied sense of how your body can work as a unified whole.

# Chapter 11

# There Are No Shortcuts, No Secrets, No Magic Pills

*[Cassius Clay] was just ordinary, and I doubt whether any scout would have thought much of him in his first year. About a year later, though, you could see that the little smart aleck—I mean, he's always been sassy—had a lot of potential... He was a kid willing to make the sacrifices necessary to achieve something worthwhile in sports. I realized it was almost impossible to discourage him. He was easily the hardest worker of any kid I ever taught.*

-Joe Martin, *Muhammad Ali's first boxing coach*

*When you get a black belt ranking it doesn't mean you've gotten a foot in the door. It means you have learned how to find the doorknob.*

-Dave Lowry

In Hollywood films, the novice pipsqueak trains furiously for a few weeks of cinematic glory compressed into ninety seconds of high-octane, sweat-filled sequences. Then, against all odds, and backed by the London Symphony Orchestra, he or she defeats the seasoned champion.

That's why it's called, fiction.

In our hurry-up world we expect too much too soon. Ours is a culture of delusion and dilettantism.

As the chapter title states, there are no shortcuts. Talent may exist, yet those with it do not fundamentally improve unless they put in their time. This is true of everybody from Michelangelo to Mohammad Ali.

If the previous statement appears to contradict the idea of working less in order to increase sense-ability, rest assured, it doesn't. Working less against yourself does not mean hardly working at all. It simply means working more intelligently so that more of your effort goes to where you want it to go.

## Steve's Story

Steve normally showed up for my weekly Taichi class after having spent the morning riding his bicycle. "I'm looking for something meditative and non-competitive," he said on his first day, before announcing that he had just ridden 26.8 miles (apparently he had an odometer on his bicycle). Like most avid cyclists I know, Steve had muscular thighs and well-defined calf muscles. And like most athletes I know, he assumed that one kind of strength could be easily morphed into another—that, for instance, the kind needed to pedal a bicycle across country roads would translate easily into the kind needed to practice Taichi.

Of course, most people assume that you don't even need strength to practice Taichi. Few people, in fact, take the art very seriously because it has become stereotyped as a slow motion sequence performed by old people. In my classes, however, students of all ages quickly discover that movements done slowly and with great precision can be very challenging. Even attending athletes have been surprised to discover that Taichi involves strengthening their bodies in ways with which they were initially unfamiliar. Regardless of their physical aptitude, I let students know that strengthening their body in new and varied ways takes learning and therefore time, exploration and effort. Strength, I tell them, can be thought of as a skill that can be learned, just like any other skill.

Unmoved by this idea, Steve would express renewed shock at the beginning of each class that a "simple" Taichi warm-up could be so challenging to someone with his tree trunk legs. Predictably, renewed shock meant renewed excuses. During his first class, for example, Steve let the class know that he could leg press more than most of his peers. "My legs are really very strong," he reassured us several times while struggling with the basic stances. I nodded in acknowledgement, noting that doing the leg press and practicing Taichi require categorically different uses of the body.

As a teacher, I'm mostly interested in how my students learn and mostly uninterested in how proficient they already are. I don't need them to boast about or demonstrate their skills when I can readily see how much strength, agility, coordination and balance they have as soon as they walk through the door. Their acture says it all. Moreover, you cannot be performing and exploring both at the same time. So if a student is busy showing-off or otherwise in performance mode, he is missing out on valuable learning.

On his eighth and what was to be, final day of class, Steve arrived as confident as ever. "I rode 30 miles this morning," he announced cheerfully. Sadly, trying to convince the class of his physical prowess continued to prevent him from paying attention to his own movements. Steve stumbled clumsily through the warm-up and seemed as hurried as ever to get through the form. Meanwhile, he continued to remind the class of how tired his legs were from his morning ride (during which he beat all of his riding partners). While he had logged in hundreds of miles on his bicycle, it was obvious that over the course of eight weeks, he had barely learned a thing about Taichi. Steve, however, seemed to think otherwise. It was time, he mentioned in parting, to move on to a "more challenging," endeavor, "now that I have a decent mastery Taichi."

## Reality Check

*If people knew how hard I worked to get my mastery, it wouldn't seem so wonderful at all.*

-Michelangelo

While all of us experience flashes of brilliance and huge leaps of improvement now and again, these flashes and leaps rest on a foundation of piecemeal and often painstaking learning that occurs over a long period of time. Hoping for significant improvement by any other means falls under the label of fantasy. Believing that you have achieved mastery by any other means is called delusion.

Of course, saying that learning takes time does not mean that you cannot improve in a very short period. It is in fact possible to experience improvement in spaces as short as five to fifteen minutes. For improvement to be lasting and deep, however, requires much more time and effort. In the end, we get to choose how lasting and deep we want our learning to go.

After many years of practicing martial arts I'm supposed to be highly skilled, and in my head, I sometimes believe I that am. Yet, what each additional year of learning gives me is a sense of how little I know and how comparatively shallow my abilities are compared to how impressive I had made them out to be. Perhaps it's because each piece of knowing puts me more in touch with how much more is out there. For even though I've put in thousands of hours of training, I've been clobbered by more than a few who have put in thousands more. And no matter how many thousands of hours I continue to train, two old masters on the other side of the ocean will always be able to toss me through the air with the greatest of ease.

I say this not to discourage you, but rather to expose the vast and joyous expanse of learning that lies ahead of anyone willing to not know the answers and not claim mastery. I notice that whenever I let go of my own need to know more and look superior it immediately opens the floodgates of learning. No longer needing to defend my "expertise" and "rightness" I feel both relieved and free to explore and discover. Even though not-knowing has a bad name in our culture, it is actually a gift that allows us to stand in wonder. Life, in fact, never really gets boring if you are willing to not know all the answers.

## Immersion Learning

Learning intensively seven days a week for a month is not only worth more than doing it once a week for a year, it is much more fun. The more concentrated the learning, the more momentum you gain and the more you find yourself wanting to do it. The more spread out the learning—a little here, a little there—the more backward steps you end up taking while trying to move forward, and less enthusiasm you will feel in practicing. I strongly believe that spreading out learning too thinly is only useful for showing you possibilities for improvement. Immersion learning, on the other hand, leads to dramatic leaps in improvement and allows you to *live* the possibilities.

One of my early immersions, mentioned in the Prologue, not only gave me my first real inkling of my learning potential, but allowed me to start living it. Training 6 hours a day, 7 days a week, brought on enormous changes that I had never imagined possible. By the end of that summer with the masters, not only was my Bagua different, but the way I stood, walked, ran and simply moved had changed so much that I felt like I had been born into a new body. And the beauty of it was that it was just the beginning: through immersion I had finally found the doorknob.

Obviously, you don't have to train 6 hours a day, 7 days a week to improve—and I generally don't encourage such rigor. To realize significant improvements, however, I do encourage that you make a concentrated effort. For four consecutive weeks, devote 45-60 minutes every day to exploring the lessons. That's equivalent to one long, or two to three short lessons per day. At most, allow yourself one day off per week from the lessons. If you find yourself overwhelmed after two weeks, take one week off and then resume. I predict that if you concentrate your explorations into two to four-week time periods, you will be happily surprised by the results. On the other hand, if you start out by thinly spreading out your lessons—doing for example, one every other week over the next six months—you will probably end up disappointed.

During your immersion, make sure you do at least one lesson from the "Throwing the Ball" series every day (Lessons 1-8). These lessons are an important foundation for running as well as many other sports. Though the lessons may initially appear simple, paying close attention to the constraints will reveal more and more how bringing awareness to even the smallest parts of your body can increase your power, speed and agility. Following the constraints in each lesson with ever greater precision will dramatically alter your walking and running over time. As always, better to explore with precision and attention for one minute than to practice without precision and without attention for a lifetime. That one minute equals sixty seconds that you get to move without your habits—move, that is, within the world of learning and discovery.

In addition to the "Throwing the Ball" series, I have categorized certain lessons by how they affect the rotation of your pelvis and spine. Your pelvis and spine have the possibility of rotating around 3 different axes: X, Y and Z (see below). Each axis is vital, not just for running and walking, but for movement in general. In Week 1, we will explore rotation around the X-Axis; in Week 2, rotation around the Y-Axis; and in week 3, rotation around the Z-Axis.

In addition to rotation, I've added the crucial element of both stabilizing and elongating your spine in Weeks 2, 3 and 4. When you are running, you want your spine to be pliable, but not floppy; elongated, but not stiff. Watch Olympic runners and you can get a sense of both stability and elongation. Notice how tall they look as they stride down the track.

Finally, it is useful to do a short lesson or even part of a lesson of your choice before your daily run (or your daily walk, if you're taking time off from running). If you're not used to running every day, try adding short runs or long walks on your usual days off.

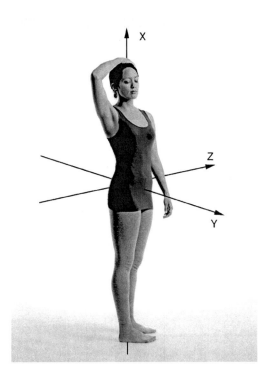

# Recommended 4-Week Lesson Plan

## Week 1

Dedicate the first week to exploring the "Throwing the Ball" lessons more intensively.

**"Throwing the Ball" lessons:**

Lesson 1:  Throwing the Ball 1:  Posing Questions
Lesson 2:  Throwing the Ball 2:  The Power of Your 1st Metatarsal
Lesson 3:  Throwing the Ball 3:  Discovering Power in Your Hips in Sidelying
Lesson 4:  Throwing the Ball 4:  Stabilizing Your Front Leg While Lying Down
Lesson 5:  Throwing the Ball 5:  Stabilizing Your Front Leg While Sitting

**X-Axis of Rotation:**

Lesson 9:  Where Does My Arm Begin?
Lesson 17:  Reach & Roll on Your Back
Lesson 12:  Mobilizing Your Ribcage

## Week 2

**"Throwing the Ball" lessons:**

Lesson 2:  Throwing the Ball 2:  The Power of Your 1st Metatarsal
Lesson 3:  Throwing the Ball 3:  Discovering Power in Your Hips in Sidelying
Lesson 4:  Throwing the Ball 4:  Stabilizing Your Front Leg While Lying Down
Lesson 5:  Throwing the Ball 5:  Stabilizing Your Front Leg While Sitting
Lesson 6:  Throwing the Ball 6:  Stabilizing Your Front Leg
Lesson 7:  Throwing the Ball 7:  Lifting All Your Toes
Lesson 8:  Throwing the Ball 8:  Eversion

**Y-Axis of Rotation:**

Lesson 16:  Salsa Hips
Lesson 12:  Mobilizing Your Ribcage

**Stabilizing and Elongating Your Spine**

Lesson 6:  Throwing the Ball 6:  Stabilizing Your Front Leg
Lesson 7:  Throwing the Ball 7:  Lifting All Your Toes

Lesson 8:   Throwing the Ball 8:  Eversion

# Week 3
**"Throwing the Ball" lessons:**
   Lesson 6:   Throwing the Ball 6:  Stabilizing Your Front Leg
   Lesson 7:   Throwing the Ball 7:  Lifting All Your Toes
   Lesson 8:   Throwing the Ball 8:  Eversion

**Z-Axis of Rotation:  Lifting Your Head**
   Lesson 10:  Standing Tall Without Trying to Stand Tall
   Lesson 12:  Mobilizing Your Ribcage
   Lesson 14:  Water Jugs, Furniture and Other Things to Carry on Your
                    Head
   Lesson 20:  Making Your Head Lighter

**Stabilizing and Elongating Your Spine:**
   Lesson 15:  Reaching for the Sky
   Lesson 18:  Boxer's Shuffle 1:  Forward and Back
   Lesson 6:   Throwing the Ball 6:  Stabilizing Your Front Leg
   Lesson 7:   Throwing the Ball 7:  Stabilizing Your Front Leg
   Lesson 8:   Throwing the Ball 8:  Stabilizing Your Front Leg

# Week 4
**Choose from any of the "Throwing the Ball" lessons:**
   Lesson 1:   Throwing the Ball 1:  Posing Questions
   Lesson 2:   Throwing the Ball 2:  The Power of Your 1st Metatarsal
   Lesson 3:   Throwing the Ball 3:  Discovering Power in Your Hips in
                    Sidelying
   Lesson 4:   Throwing the Ball 4:  Stabilizing Your Front Leg While Ly-
                    ing Down
   Lesson 5:   Throwing the Ball 5:  Stabilizing Your Front Leg While Sit-
                    ting
   Lesson 6:   Throwing the Ball 6:  Stabilizing Your Front Leg
   Lesson 7:   Throwing the Ball 7:  Stabilizing Your Front Leg
   Lesson 8:   Throwing the Ball 8:  Stabilizing Your Front Leg

**Explore any of the 3-Axes of Rotation (try a different axis every day)**
**Stabilizing and Elongating Your Spine:**
   Lesson 15:  Reaching for the Sky
   Lesson 18:  Boxer's Shuffle 1:  Forward and Back
   Lesson 19:  Boxer's Shuffle 2:  Side to Side

# Chapter 12

# Running With Your Rear End

*For every action, there is an equal and opposite reaction.*

-Isaac Newton's Third Law of Motion (simplified)


After watching runners for several years I have come to realize that most rely on the power of their calf muscles and/or hip flexors (the muscles that draw your knee up toward your chest) to propel themselves forward. In either case, what runners normally neglect is the most powerful muscle group in the human body.

Situated in your rear end, gluteal muscles are designed to extend each hip by pulling the thigh backward (see below). Hip extension does two things at once. First, it helps to thrust your whole body forward with a tremendous amount of force.

Second the backward pulling of one thigh can work in synchrony with the flexion, or forward and upward pushing of the opposite thigh. This means that the backward motion of one thigh actually helps to drive the forward and upward motion of the other. And this collective action of the two thighs is in large part what gives great runners their "lift" and makes it look as if they are floating effortlessly. The symbiosis, or lack thereof, also explains why many people have difficulty lifting their knees when they run: like me in my track days, they do not understand how to extend their hips while in full stride.

Try Lesson 17 ("Reaching & Roll on Your Back") to get a clearer feeling of how to extend your hips powerfully. When you are finished go for a short run and notice how each knee travels as you push back with the opposite leg. Are your knees moving higher and/or further forward almost by default? Do you feel more power in your stride?

## Pushing Off With Your Rear End

To create the abovementioned "lift" while running requires not just extending one hip while flexing the other, but coordinating the two with the rolling of each foot as it pushes off the ground.

Calf muscles are designed to play an auxiliary, rather than primary role in pushing off. Specifically, their movement is designed to work symbiotically with your rear end to help mobilize the gluteal muscles. Here's how it works: as you stride forward, the function of your calf muscles is to complement hip extension (the movement that pulls your thigh backward) while they push the ball of your foot downward and backward at the same time. [see figure w] The downward and backward movement of the ball of your foot, in other words, works in coordination with the contraction of your gluteal muscles to pull your thigh backward, and this in turn helps to push your opposite thigh forward and upward with great force. If for some reason your calf muscles are not working in coordination with the rest of you, your hips will not extend fully and you will have less driving force, the result of which will be a shorter, more laborious stride.

Obviously, for calf muscles to function in coordination with the rest of you, it is not enough to simply contract them in isolation, but to contract them in synchrony with the flexion-extension (bending-straightening) of your hips and the flexion-extension (bending-straightening) of your knees. Unfortunately, while many people know how to contract their calves, they neither know how fully extend their hips, nor fully flex their knees, and this results in a group of relatively small muscles—namely the soleus and gastrocnemius—having to do what they are not designed to do—namely perform the bulk of the work. And when smaller muscles have to take over work for which they are not designed, two things occur: 1) you get far less power because the larger muscles are not fully participating; and 2) the smaller muscles quickly become overworked. Thus, while the gluteal muscles may receive a perennial vacation in such cases, the calf muscles work overtime and consequently become short, tight and quickly fatigued. Many people complaining of tight calf muscles stretch them frequently to no avail, not realizing that were they to learn how to fully extend their hips, and fully bend their knees, their poor calf muscles would be given a chance to rest and function in the way that they were designed to—that is, to play a complementary rather than leading role in the push off.

You can easily identify "calf pushers" because it looks as if they are shuffling when they are actually trying to run. I, myself, can both identify and identify with such people because this is exactly how I used to run. Obviously, I ran this way, not because I wanted to shuffle, but because I simply knew no other way.

Exploring Lesson 11 ("Lift Your Knees") and Lesson 17 ("Reach & Roll on Your Back"), along with the Lessons 1-8 (The "Throwing the Ball" series) will help you to gain a profound, embodied understanding of how to run with your rear end.

## Evolution (or God) Doesn't Make Mistakes

In certain parts of the world where individuals travel long distances on foot without the "advantage" of expensive running shoes, and perform daily activities such as eating, socializing and resting, by sitting on their haunches, people tend to maintain a far wider range of motion and more refined sense-abilities than those living in the midst of modern comforts. As a result, the former tend to exhibit superior acture, gait and stride. While it is not proven, I believe many of the great runners from Kenya, Ethiopia, Morocco and South Africa owe at least some of their achievement not only to an incredible work ethic, but the fact that daily life in these regions often necessitates having greater sense-ability in the movement of everything from head to literal toe.

In contrast, the overwhelming majority of people I've either observed or directly worked with in the U.S.—including professional dancers and highly trained athletes—tend to exhibit stunted sense-abilities resulting from a modern lifestyle that underutilizes certain muscles in the body. In our culture, one part that appears to be universally neglected is the feet. Specifically, we have stopped using the muscles and tendons that reach from our shins to the tops of our feet and tops of our toes. I will go as far as to say that in modern U.S. culture, we unconsciously behave as if these muscles and tendons do not exist. Yet evolution (or God) didn't put them there by mistake. Every single muscle is absolutely vital for the full and potent functioning of your entire body. When the abovementioned muscles atrophy, signaling the extinction of corresponding neural pathways that control them, it can dramatically alter the way you stand, walk and run.

To illustrate this, I return once again to our first principle of movement (which also happens to be Newton's Third Law of Motion): for every action, there is an equal and opposite reaction. Consider that pushing down into the earth with the ball of your foot requires a certain lifting up of some other part of your foot. What part could that be?

Normally when we push off, we don't use the entire ball of the foot. Certain joints in the ball of your foot (the joints that connect your metatarsals to your toes) normally play a larger role in pushing into the earth as others lift off. In order to push, down, there must be a pulling up. And the more forcefully you want to push down with one part, the more forcefully you want to be able to pull up with another. If the muscles that deal with the pulling up have become atrophied, your pushing down will feel murky and less powerful.

Try any of the lessons in the "Throwing the Ball" series (Lessons 1-8) to see how reawakening and reinvigorating the muscles and tendons on the tops of your feet give you more balance, fluidity and propulsion in walking and running (you'll also notice how it helps you balance in standing). At some point when you have finished the "Throwing the Ball" series, you may choose to explore the "Boxer's Shuffle" series (Lessons 18 and 19), which is a continuation of the sensorimotor concepts introduced in "Throwing the Ball."

Each of the lessons in both the "Throwing the Ball" and "Boxer's Shuffle" series is designed to help you discover the relationship between hip extension and pushing through the ball of the foot with the help of the calf muscles. In addition, each of these lessons reinvigorates the relationship between the muscles on the top of your foot and the entire rest of your leg and pelvis. By exploring the lessons, you will begin to experience far greater power in your push-off while relieving your calves of unnecessary stress and strain. As a side benefit, the lessons will help tremendously in strengthening your feet and ankles, thereby improving your balance and helping to prevent ankle sprains.

## Running With Your Upper Body

Hip extension and the tops of our feet are not the only things that we tend to neglect when running. Many overlook the role of the upper body thinking that it's the legs that should be doing all the work. And your legs really do do all the work yet provide less power when your upper body isn't involved. This is because it is impossible to stride powerfully and freely without the full cooperation of your upper body. The thrusting of your rear end and the lifting of your knees must, in other words, occur in complete coordination with, not only the swinging of your arms, but the rotation, flexion and extension of different parts of your entire spine. And if your chest, back, arms, shoulders and neck are not working in coordination with the driving of your knees forward and up (and the simultaneous driving of your metatarsals backward and downward), they end up working against your legs, making them feel both weaker and heavier. The effect is akin to running with a sled tied to your hips.

As I mentioned before, your pelvis acts like the Grand Central Station of force vectors, delivering force in all directions between different parts of your body. Your pelvis, in other words, translates force all the way from your right shoulder down to your left big toe and your left heel all the way up to the top of your head. In this manner, each part of your body has the potential to either cooperate or conflict with parts that aren't directly connected to it. If your upper body is in agreement with what's below your waist, your entire body will be propelled forward with enormous force. But if the two are not cooperating—that is, if you are holding excess tension, or parts of you are not doing their proper share of work (earlier I mentioned that when you don't know how to properly extend your hips, your calf muscles have to take on more work than they are designed for), you end up with internal conflict and force that would otherwise propel you forward gets dampened. Naturally, you will feel weaker since you are, in a sense, restraining your own power.

If you watch good runners you will notice that they are naturally upright and their upper bodies relaxed. Their stride exudes a certain ease and gracefulness that all of us can emulate when we start to feel how our upper body is able to cooperate with the rest of us. When your arms, shoulders, back and chest are in sync with your pelvis and legs, you will have a wonderful feeling of comfort and power throughout your entire body. You will feel tall without trying to make yourself tall. Your elbows will feel like they are pumping automatically, as if by themselves. Your stride will feel smooth and graceful.

Both Lesson 11 ("Lift Your Knees") and Lesson 12 ("Mobilizing Your Ribcage") will help you to integrate the movement of your arms, shoulders and ribcage with the movement of your legs. In addition, all of the lessons that involve stabilizing and elongating your spine will give you a sense of how important your upper body is in creating more "lift" and power in your legs. The stabilizing and elongating lessons include: Lesson 15 ("Reaching for the Sky"), the last three lessons from the "Throwing the Ball" series, and the two lessons from the "Boxer's Shuffle" series.

# Chapter 13

# Running With Both Ends

*They found that the women could carry 20 percent of their own body weight [on top of their head] with no additional exertion.*

-Otto Pohl, *Improving the Way Humans Walk,*
New York Times, *March 12, 2002*

Despite advocating slowing down for the last twelve chapters, I too, often feel the pressure to speed up. Hurrying still creeps into my life when my mind gets wrapped up being somewhere else, doing something else, and thereby prevents me from paying attention to what's in front of my nose. When something feels too challenging, for example, my habit is to either try to get it over with as quickly as possible, or avoid doing it altogether. This used to be my approach to hills—going up them, that is. Of course, hurrying up hills made the experience much less interesting and fruitful because in my haste I failed to realize that the way I was bulldozing through them—rather than lightly bounding up them—actually slowed me down and used up more energy in the process. Furthermore, I lost out on the enjoyment I could have been having—and yes, running up hills can be fun, though your enjoyment will depend on how you do it and whether or not you are forcing yourself.

A few summers ago while visiting my parents in San Diego, I challenged myself to make a nearby and very steep hill part of my daily run. After the first day I ended up with very sore Achilles tendons. They were so sore in fact, that I found myself limping through my daily run for the rest of the week. I began to worry.

Is this a sign of congenital weakness? Perhaps this is part of the "aging process" that everyone talks about. Maybe I should seek expert advice. It didn't help that I knew several men my age who had torn their Achilles tendons while playing sports. One physician friend had even told me that a torn Achilles is quite common to men in their 40s.

After re-examining how I was running up the hill, I realized that by trying to get it over with, I ended up leaning too far forward and consequently relied too much on my calf muscles. By trying to bulldoze my way through, in other words, I didn't follow my own principle of running with my rear end. Excited that I may have seen through one of my blind own spots, I decided to use the same hill as a playground. What I was looking for was a way to engage my rear end more and in the process give my calf muscles, and consequently, Achilles tendons, a chance to rest.

First off, I had to give up on the idea of covering as much ground as quickly as possible—or more succinctly, getting it over with. By going too fast I couldn't feel what I was doing and therefore didn't know what I was doing. Slowing down and being playful allowed me to start to feel what I hadn't felt when I was too hurried. Taking my time to play created space for me to move in non-habitual ways.

Over the next few days I was delighted to discover much more power in my stride when running uphill. And I was tremendously relieved when the soreness in my Achilles tendons began to subside almost immediately.

Go to Lesson 13 ("Using Your Butt to Lift You Up") if you want to discover how much more power you can generate by simply changing your intention as you run uphill.

Discomfort can often be seen as a signpost reminding you that there is a better way. Sometimes it is more of a detour than a signpost, as in my case when my Achilles tendons were so tender that I was forced to slow down. My slowing down and subsequent experimentation not only helped my Achilles tendons to heal, but allowed me to make new discoveries that in the end allowed me to run faster.

## Where Does My Head Begin?

How you carry your head affects the movement of everything down to your feet. As a result your head plays an important role in how you use your legs and thus, how much power you gain in your stride. To get a sense of what how your feet must adjust to the movement of your head, turn a broom upside down and hold the handle with one hand. Notice how much work you have to do with your hand just to keep the broom from tipping over. Even the smallest movement at the top of the inverted broom requires you to make large adjustments all the way at the bottom, where your hand is.

In order to better understand the connection between the position of your head and how it affects your standing, walking and running, you first need to feel what's going on. Go to Lesson 14 ("Water Jugs, Furniture and Other Things to Carry on Your Head") if you want a better sense of how even the smallest deviations in how you carry your head affect your posture and thus, the way you move.

## Running with Your Head

Leaning forward is one of the most popular ways of hurrying when you're on two feet. I've noticed that most people not only lean forward when they walk and run on flat terrain, but they do it when going uphill as well. Many, in fact, lean even more on the uphills. Yet, as mentioned in Chapter 8 ("Imitation: Why Trying to Run Like an Olympian Keeps You From Running Like an Olympian"), whether or not leaning works for you depends crucially on exactly how you do it. It is quite common, for instance, to collapse the back of your neck when leaning, and as stated in Lesson 14 ("Water Jugs, Furniture and Other Things to Carry on Your Head"), if the back of your neck is collapsing your *Baihui* isn't reaching for the sky. If your *Baihui* isn't reaching for the sky, the resultant configuration of your spine will be unsound, perhaps akin to a toppling or collapsing building. Not only is this type of configuration bad for your back and neck, but it saps your entire body of power.

Instead of leaning, I recommend exploring different ways to carry your head. One approach is to rise from the center crown—the previously mentioned *Baihui* point. Whenever I remember to lift from my *Baihui*, it instantly feels as if someone has just added "turbo charge" to my engine. The feeling of a "turbo boost" becomes especially pronounced when going uphill. To get a sense of the increase in thrust that can result from how you carry your head, go to Lesson 15 ("Reaching for the Sky").

Finally, the relationship between head, neck and spine brings up the rarely talked about issue of giving your knees enough "room" to lift. Because leaning tends to restrain extension in the hip that is thrusting backward and downward, while at the same time hampering the driving force of the hip/knee that is moving forward and upward, people who bend too far forward may feel like their upper body is getting in the way of their knees. Your spine, in other words, must be sufficiently erect to sufficiently extend one hip while flexing the other in a manner that maximizes propulsion. This is why even though sprinters lean way forward in the starting blocks, they do not remain there after the gun has fired. Once they leave the blocks, they very quickly come to an upright position, thereby creating more "room" for their knees to drive both forward and upward.* Staying upright and not leaning allows them to generate much more thrust in each stride. Step 5 of Lesson 11 ("Lift Your Knees") will give you a clearer sense of how you can lose thrust by leaning too far forward.

---

* Michael Johnson and Jesse Owens remain the two most prominent examples of a tall and upright style of running.

# Chapter 14

# Running Shoes

*"Johnny Quest," brought to you by P.F. Flyers with the "magic wedge" that helps you run your fastest and jump your highest.*

-1960s TV advertisement

*New from Sketchers, Shape-ups are the first stylish shoes that actually promote better health.... A stronger you: building and toning muscles from your back and abdomen to your thighs and calves. A healthier you: improving circulation, burning calories and losing weight. A more attractive you: Shape-ups reduce cellulite and promote good posture...*

-2010 TV advertisement

Our ancestors did not evolve with hundred-dollar running shoes attached to their feet and world-class runners like Zola Budd and Sydney Maree didn't use them for most of their formative years. So why do we need them today?

Function and structure reinforce each other in a reciprocal manner. How you walk and run, for example, will determine the wear pattern in the bottom of your shoes. Likewise, the structure of your shoes will largely circumscribe how you walk and run. So when you impose on your feet the structure of say, a new pair of running shoes, it will affect the functioning of your entire body. The support from your shoes, for example, forces your entire body to adjust while at the same time immobilizing many joints in your feet and ankles. The padding in your shoes serves to displace shock and consequently acts as a substitute for how you would otherwise use the muscles and tendons surrounding the joints in your feet, ankles, knees, pelvis and spine to redirect the incoming force. The elevation in the heels of the shoes serves to tilt your body forward as if you were standing on a hillside facing away from the hillside. As your nervous system gets accustomed to standing on this artificial slope, all of the muscles from your heels to the base of your skull shorten and remain short in response. Most of us don't notice the shortening except in rare instances when we try to touch our toes, sit on our haunches (that is, squat with our heels still touching the floor) or do a somersault. What we more likely notice, however, is the tightness and fatigue in our calf muscles, or perhaps how uncomfortable our lower backs feel.

Shoes are to your feet what earplugs are to your hearing: while both protect you, that protection also serves to insulate your sense-abilities from the outside world. Generally speaking, shoes tend to limit the range of motion in your joints, and muffle the sensory input that would otherwise register below your knees. Here, it's important to note that your muscles, tendons and joint surfaces do not exist in isolation. They are, in fact, attached to your nervous system and cannot function without it. So when you begin to limit the variety of choices for your muscles and tendons, you are also limiting the amount of movement patterns available to your brain. A simplistic view of it goes as follows: where unused muscles and tendons gradually become stiff and weak, neural pathways that once governed the varied movement of these muscles and tendons begin to die off. And as neural pathways die off, sense-ability atrophies and movement patterns begin to disappear from your repertoire. For many people the result is having not only weaker, but clumsier feet and ankles, which in turn translates to a weaker stride.

## Strengthening Your Feet Sense-ably

The possible effect of well-supported shoes does not, of course, mean that you cannot be a good or even great runner if you wear them.* As you have surely noticed, virtually everybody, including Olympic champions, is touting the latest "technological advances" in footwear. The likelihood of developing weaker feet, a less powerful stride and self-destructive movement habits, however, is much higher in a culture such as ours, which encourages everyone to not only wear shoes, but highly supported ones with an elevated heel from an early age. Compared to people who grow up wearing no shoes, or only the flimsiest of footwear, we not only have weaker and more rigid feet and ankles, but walk and run with less stability and power. Thus for us shoe-wearers, it is particularly useful to find ways to strengthen our feet and mobilize joints down there that have become stiff and inflexible over the years.

Finally, if we accept the previously stated theme that the movement of

---

* For people with loose ligaments, well-supported shoes can even enhance the stability in their feet in ways that their own muscles are not yet able to (I insert "yet" here because it is possible for these people to gradually learn to use their muscles to create that stability). In such cases having a good deal of support may actually be beneficial by conferring added stability where none previously existed.

one part of your body affects the movement of all other parts (see Chapter 10: "Following Instructions: Where Do My Knees Begin?"), we can understand that changing the way you use your feet will alter the way you use your entire body—all the way to the top of your head.

Take note that what you've just read is absolutely not a message to throw out your running shoes and go run ten miles in bare feet or in flimsy sneakers. Doing so would almost certainly result in injury because your body has already become not only accustomed to having a great deal of support, but dependent on it. The muscles and tendons in your feet and legs, for example, lack the strength and flexibility to deal with losing this support. Your entire spine has become accustomed to a more limited range of motion that is part and parcel to wearing shoes.* Obviously, it would be a shock to your entire system—muscles, tendons, ligaments and mind—because you cannot in one split second magically acquire the sense-ability necessary to adapt to such startling new conditions. Since years of wearing shoes have led to your current state it will take at least a little time for your feet, spine and nervous system to re-gain some of the independence they probably once had in early childhood.

If you want to experiment with wearing less support, I recommend you start off by doing it for short periods. You can for example, try walking for short distances in an old pair of Converse All-Stars. If you are willing to spend a little money, you can begin experimenting with the newest type of shoes exhibiting "five fingers" that have virtually no support and thus allow for a much fuller range of motion in your feet, ankles and spine. When at home, you can try walking and standing in bare feet (or in socks) for short periods and over time, extend those periods.

Take note that in all my suggestions you are encouraged to initially walk, not run. Once you have become accustomed to walking with less support, you can experiment with running very short distances—maybe a few steps at a time to start with—and working your way up to 50 meters at a time. As long as you are gradual in building up distance, you will maximize improvement while minimizing the risk of injury.

The lessons in the "Throwing the Ball" series (Lessons 1-8) are among my favorites for helping students gain better awareness of how their feet, and even toes, relate to the rest of their body. Each of the lessons works very effectively in strengthening, not only your feet, ankles and lower legs, but your thighs and gluteal region as well. As a side benefit from doing the lessons, the greater control in your legs, along with increased rotational force in your hips and spine will likely improve your performance in other sports and even daily activities. And whether or not you actually engage in other sports, you will nonetheless feel a marked difference in the

---

* Your entire spine needs to adjust to standing, walking and running in bare feet. If it does not make the proper adjustments—and it won't simply do so without a period of learning—your feet will strike the ground with a resounding thud sending shock waves all the way up to your head.

way you stand and walk in the short time it takes to do just one lesson.

## Everything Below Something is a Foundation For That Something

As mentioned in Chapter 5 ("Intention"), our first principle of movement—"for every action, there is an equal and opposite reaction"—ensures that everything in your body works in a reciprocal fashion. Everything on top affects everything on the bottom and vice versa. You could say that something below something else acts like a foundation for that something else. Thus, your feet act as a foundation for your ankles and your ankles for your knees. Weakness in any of the foundations will cause a chain reaction all the way up to the top of your head. Since your shoes form the final foundation between you and the ground it is important that they form a secure base. If either shoe tilts even the smallest amount to the right or left, for example, everything above it must adjust. Believe it or not, even your other foot and leg will be affected. Any unevenness in either shoe, in other words, requires your entire body to compensate, which could translate to overusing certain muscles while under-using others. And the consequent muscle imbalances can, over time, lead to uneven wear and tear in your joints.

Your movement habits involve a multitude of factors including the way each foot lands and pushes off, and all the intricacies that make this happen, from how your ankle joints articulate, to the contraction of your hamstrings, to whether your head is cocked a fraction of an inch to one side. Too much uneven wear in your shoes and you will start to exaggerate these habits, reinforcing movement patterns that may be inefficient and possibly damaging in the long run. This is perhaps most obvious in people who have collapsed arches. If you look at the shoes of somebody with flat feet, you will likely see that the wear and compression patterns in the tread and sole reinforce their particular way of grinding their ankles and knees. The effect doesn't stop there, but actually continues up to the hips, pelvis, spinal cord and eventually, head.*

Of course, most of us do not produce such extreme wear patterns on our shoes. We do have our own characteristic ways of wearing out shoes, however, that if gone unchecked will reinforce any imbalances we may already exhibit, or even create ones where none had previously existed. In light of this, I urge you to examine how you feel during and after a run, considering that wear patterns can contribute to discomfort as well as decreases in power.

---

*It is important to note here that in the vast majority of cases, flat feet have much more to do with unhealthy habits and muted sense-abilities than with genetics. I strongly believe that it is possible to improve the strength and flexibility of your arches by learning new ways to use your feet, ankles and indeed, entire body. Considering that flat feet are a symptom of atrophied muscles and lowered sense-ability, learning could be an effective way to literally raise the arches. Lessons 1-8 from the "Throwing the Ball" series can be very effective in improving the strength and pliability of your feet. Exploring these lessons can, over an extended period time, begin to raise your arches if they are weak or fallen. I have seen my own previously low arches grow significantly since I began experimenting with the way I use my feet.

I encourage you to play around with different types of shoes and take your time getting used to whatever it is you put on your feet. Take everything as an experiment—one in which by exploring movement slowly, you are creating new neural pathways that simultaneously lead to a more balance and a powerful stride. Try, for example, walking around without your insoles and see what happens. Spend five minutes in shoes with a lot of padding and notice how it affects your push-off compared to five minutes in shoes with little to no padding, such as racing flats. Take a few steps in super-slow motion—as if doing Taichi—and see how this feels in bare feet compared to when wearing shoes.* Whatever style of shoe you play with and whatever movements you make, notice if you feel more or less of the ground as a result. See if you have more or less control over your feet and legs. Notice if your joints feel more or less comfortable. Sense how seemingly minor changes actually affect the way your feet land and push off. If you try shoes with less support, or walk for longer periods in bare feet, you will be employing muscles and tendons that haven't been used in a long time. Your feet may initially tire more quickly as a result, but they will continue to get stronger as long as you don't push yourself too much. And this brings me to the most important point: be gentle with yourself and don't turn play into a chore or you will risk injury. Consider that changing shoes is simply an option, not a necessity. You may in fact love your current style of footwear and never want to change.

Lesson 16 ("Salsa Hips") will help you discover how a supple ribcage improves smoothness and power in your stride. This is a particularly useful lesson if you are transitioning to shoes with less padding, or even considering joining the barefoot running movement.

---

* Every time you change what's on your feet, your nervous system has to readjust itself. The less accustomed you are to whatever you are wearing, the more time it will take to adjust. I notice a huge difference in the way my foot strikes the ground and the way my upper body wants to move whenever switching from my usual pair of worn sneakers to a new pair, or a different style of sneakers with less of a sole, or to dress shoes, which tend to have higher heels, more padding and less flexibility in the sole. Dress shoes normally make me feel clunky at first, while my feet, legs and spine are finding ways to accommodate the new foundation under my feet. In contrast, shoes that have minimal padding and more flexibility in the sole give me a tremendous boost in my push-off as well as a great deal more maneuverability. In either case, however, I am continuously listening to my ankles, knees, pelvis and spine so that they can adjust to the change.

# Part III: More Life

(Skip this part if you are still in a hurry)

# Chapter 15

# Compulsion

*I am always against "no pain, no gain." Because pain is always the body rejecting whatever you are doing. It's your body telling you, "I don't want to do it, it's not right for me." But people can force themselves to do it, sometimes because they come from a hard life, and have had to work so hard just to survive. That becomes the mentality, therefore anything you do must become hard, uncomfortable. That is not a good thing.*

-Fong Ha, 5th Generation Yang-Style Taichi Master

Like many newcomers to Feldenkrais, I expected instant results. Most people come seeking help with injuries and pain. I came because when I read Dr. Feldenkrais' book on compulsion, I knew he was talking about me.

It was the second week of my Professional Feldenkrais Training and our director, Frank Wildman, was leading us through another series of what were supposed to be gentle movements on the floor. After five minutes, my neck started to hurt. Yet, through gritted teeth, I persevered.

Ten minutes later and still following Frank's instructions, my neck hurt worse. If I'm doing everything right why does it hurt so much? When Frank walked by, I flagged him down.

"My neck hurts," I said helplessly, as if expecting him to wave a magic wand and instantly make the pain disappear.

Frank stopped in his tracks and looked directly at me. "Stop," he said, then turned and walked away.*

---

* Apparently, "stop" is a phrase commonly issued not only by Bagua masters, but Feldenkrais Practitioners as

The one thing I didn't consider.

Looking back now, I realize how hard I was trying to be a good student. I felt compelled to follow every instruction to a "T" lest I miss out, or look bad in Frank's or someone else's eyes. Today it seems totally comical that I was ready to tear my head off its moorings for the sake of following instructions. In reality, both my (mis)interpretation of the instructions and the need to "just do it," not only resulted in pain, but prevented me from learning. Rather than tuning into my senses, I was on autopilot, trying to "get it over with."

## Stress, Anxiety and Perception

After teaching for many years, I've noticed that losing one's senses is a common coping strategy. The process is akin to working on an assembly line where you put together gadgets as they pass by on a conveyor belt. At slow speeds, the work is manageable. But what happens when the conveyor belt starts to go faster? You have to go faster to keep up, and at some point your level of anxiety will increase very quickly. Meanwhile your ability to sense and feel will decrease proportionally and your work will get sloppier and sloppier. Ironically, because your perception is decreasing to a pinpoint, you won't notice the button in front of your face that says, "Push to stop the conveyor belt." And you won't hear the voice over the loudspeakers saying, "This is all a game. Please don't take it too seriously."

Inability to deal with stress leads to anxiety, which in turn mutes perception—the vital tool for dealing with stress. So generally speaking, the more pressure you feel, the higher your anxiety level; the higher your anxiety, the less you can sense and feel; the less you sense and feel, the less you are capable of dealing well with stress. It is a vicious cycle.

Considering that much of modern life has become some version of gadgets whizzing by on a conveyor belt, it should be no surprise that most of us are in a terrific hurry. It is a surprise to many, however, that hurrying makes us less competent to deal with the conveyor belt.

## Another Way

> *Do not depend on the hope of results. When you are doing the sort of work you have taken on...you may have to face the fact that your work will be apparently worthless and even achieve no result at all, if not perhaps results opposite to what you expect. As you get used to this idea you start more and more to concentrate not on the results but on the value, the rightness, the truth of the work itself.*

---

well.

-Thomas Merton

*Play does not require willpower to stay focused and overcome our natural desires; it is natural desire manifest. When we play, we are willing to try things without guarantee of their eventual usefulness or value; yet paradoxically, it is precisely when we let go of such motivations that we produce the things of greatest use.*

-Charles Eisenstein

Many people don't enjoy running as much as they could because they do it in ways that aren't so pleasurable. On top of that, many force themselves to do it when they really don't want to. Yet, what if there were ways to train that gave you more pleasure and you just hadn't discovered them yet? And what if, unbelievably, some of these training methods translated to running exactly the way you wanted to, when you wanted to? Wouldn't you then be delighted whenever it came time to go for a run? Naturally, if you associated running with lightness, freedom, breathing fresh outdoor air or a challenge that you were up to (rather than one that overwhelmed you), then running would become something you were always eager to do.

If you look at children running around on the playground, you won't see grim expressions on their faces (compare children's expressions to the ones you see on the faces of most adults). How do children do it? Do they ever look at adults and wonder how so many of us have managed to turn what could be play into drudgery?

Unlike children, we don't do what we want. Specifically, whereas we tend to want results and ignore the process, children care less about results and fully live the process. And in doing so, they allow themselves to move in any manner they like, sometimes trotting, sometimes skipping, sometimes hopping or jumping or rolling on the ground or spinning in circles or stopping or chasing each other or doing cartwheels or kicking their own bottoms as they move about. Is it any wonder they find so much pleasure in running?

## The All-or-Nothing Approach

We don't do what we want because we don't actually know what we want. And we don't know what we want because most of us have been forcing ourselves to do what we don't want for so long that we have come to see the world as black or white, all or nothing, either I run five miles or I don't run at all. If we want to start enjoying running more, we have to stop forcing ourselves and begin looking between the all and the nothing.

At this point you may be thinking, If I don't force myself, I won't do it! Yes, this is a possibility, but only because most of us haven't made distinctions between different ways to run. You see most of us have been attending the ever more hurried assembly line of modern life for so long that our perception has become severely narrowed. As a result, we tend to look at running—and indeed, the rest of life—as a choice of all or nothing. You can observe such narrowing every day when for example, somebody from the Midwest says, "People from LA are terrible drivers!" or someone from LA says, "People from the Midwest can't drive!" Implicit in each statement is the grouping of all people from LA or the Midwest being one way or another. Similarly, when we make running a grim reality of life that we need to do to get in shape, feel good about ourselves, improve circulation, have friends, attract a mate, or something else, we are unconsciously deciding that all types of running are grim.

In other words, by assuming that our approach to running is the only way, we are unwittingly neglecting every other way to do it. We are ignoring the fact that between the all and the nothing, there is actually a lot of something.

## How to Get Yourself Off the Couch

"But what about times when you can't get yourself off the couch?" you might be asking. "Wouldn't you be better off forcing yourself?"

Here again, we have an all-or-nothing situation. There are many ways to get off the couch. The ones most often used are on the compulsive side of will-power. But there are many other ways that involve the loving side of willpower.

One of the reasons we have trouble getting ourselves off the couch to begin with has to do with our compulsive all-or-nothing conditioning. Who wouldn't want to sit on the couch watching TV if the other alternative is to suffer through another bout of self-torture? In this case, you are sensible not to get off the couch.

Most of the exercise and training programs I have witnessed or personally experienced (some were of my own design) have to do with either whipping yourself into condition, or more likely, having someone else do the whipping for you. You'll notice that gym memberships peak right after the New Year when everybody's made a resolution to get in shape and lose weight, but attendance plummets shortly after the first month. Is it because people are lazy?

Maybe. Or maybe it's because people are sensible. That is, they are still sense-able enough to know that lashes on the back are generally no good for you, even if you happen to be the one holding the whip. Of course, this is not to say that pushing yourself, being coached and having discipline are intrinsically bad— in fact, both the prologue and Chapter 11 ("There Are No Shortcuts, No Secrets, No Magic Pills") address the positive side of discipline. Rather what I am saying is that most of us require much less, if indeed any prodding or coercion to get off the couch. Few exercise and running programs nevertheless, start at a manage-able pace for the individual. They are highly generalized to zip people into shape as fast as possible with little or no regard to learning or fundamentally improving stride, coordination, balance and agility. Obviously, starting this quickly is going to require a good deal of prodding. Considering the number of drop-outs, how-ever, starting this quickly is not the best way for everyone.

Even if I am highly disciplined and willing to be my own drill sergeant, I will run into strict physical and emotional limitations. Though I may get in shape and improve rapidly at first, my improvement will still be limited by my resis-tance to the pushing. Overcoming resistance doesn't mean that either the resis-tance itself or the attendant faulty mechanical habits have magically disappeared. Unless I allow myself to slow down and tune into my senses, both will continue to weigh down on my stride, preventing me from becoming nearly as fast and powerful as I could be. Moreover, the pressure I put on myself will likely lead me to associate running with suffering. As a result, I may never truly enjoy the activ-ity and unwittingly find myself wanting to avoid it. And when I actually succeed in avoiding it—taking a day off, for example—I may feel defeated and unworthy.

## Leading with Desire vs. Pushing with Compulsion

As I mentioned above, people embarking on a new training regimen often find themselves in over their heads. Because their initial exposure to running may have been too strenuous, they may have unconsciously stereotyped the activity to be something that requires a high tolerance for pain and suffering. In this re-gard, I recommend that workouts not be overwhelming lest they inspire fear and loathing in the person performing them. In high school, I myself feared "hard days" precisely because I had been overwhelmed by previous experiences. Even when training on my own, I often set the bar too high, believing if I didn't run fast enough and far enough, the workout wasn't any good. Training like this too often was very effective in taking all the joy out of running, though not so effec-tive in making me want to get off the couch. Indeed, during the summers when I trained alone, I would procrastinate all day and put off my runs until the evening.

This attitude stands in sharp contrast to my experience with tennis and basketball—two sports I took up after quitting track and triathloning. Rather than drearily looking ahead toward my next engagement, I would be brimming with eagerness and excitement. The very thought of playing either sport would send my heart leaping. You'll notice that people engaging in a sport that they love never identify that particular sport with dreariness (and if they do, it is likely because they are turning play in to drudgery by focusing too much on extrinsic rewards). Yet people who love their sport run enormous amounts on the court—often to the extent that they find themselves gasping for air. They do all this will-ingly and out of desire, not compulsion.

For those who do not respond well to being pushed—and I believe this is most of us—what we need is to be led in a way that allows us to bring the love back into running. Like children who slow down or walk when they are tired but on the other hand, rarely need to be encouraged to run, we need to listen to our senses. In this manner we will rediscover our own pacing and increase our distance and workout intensity in a manner that suits our individual desires.*

## Running for the Pleasure of It

Try the following experiment.

**Part I**

Go to a track where you can watch good runners in motion. It could even be where a local college team is practicing since college runners normally have good form. If that isn't available, consider that the best high school track athletes eventually end up on college teams. Watch these athletes if possible. It is not imperative that you watch good runners, but one reason for doing so is because it is so beautiful and inspiring.

If there are no convenient places to watch runners, you can tape a televised track meet where you can observe world-class runners in action. Another option is to observe your favorite runners on the Youtube.

Either way, observe how they are running without any intention of doing anything other than enjoying the experience of seeing prime athletes in action. Watch for at least 15 minutes. Then put on your running shoes and begin the second part of the experiment.

**Part II**

Begin by walking down the street simply noticing something new. It could be the smell of the grass, or flowers blooming. It could be the sound of a bird singing, the distant roar of cars from the highway, or clouds passing overhead.

Now start to pay attention to yourself. Choose one place in your body and sense how it is moving. For example, how are you pushing off with your right foot? Or, what is your left shoulder doing as you step forward with your left foot? Continue paying attention to yourself, either staying with the same part of your body or sensing other parts. Continue for at least ten minutes (carry a watch so that you can time yourself). After ten minutes you may notice that your pace has changed. Perhaps it has gotten faster. Perhaps slower. Notice if you are feeling more alive and interested in your own movement. Have your posture and gait changed?

At this point, decide whether or not to continue on your walk. If you don't, simply walk home. Whether or not you go home at this point, continue paying attention and noticing things. Those of you who choose to walk further, continue as long as you like before returning home. But the key here is not to run.

---

* If you are near the ocean, try the "Chasing and Being Chased by Waves" game at the end of Chapter 6 ("Have You Lost Your Senses?"), or make up your own game where your attention is on something other than burning calories or putting in miles.

When you get home, notice if you have the urge to run. Listen intently and try to discern what is your head and what is your heart: that is, what is compulsion and what is desire.

Wait 30 minutes. Then ask yourself again if you want to run. Whether or not you do, don't do it.

Now the next important step is not to run and the following day you will see why.

On the following day, repeat the entire process—including Part I—up until you return home. This time if you have a tremendous urge to go running you may start, but, you may only run for one block. This means that you must make the most of this one block. You will probably want to find a way to make it really enjoyable since you're only allowed one block. When you have finished, walk home.

Continue this process increasing by one block per day until you've reached the seventh day. By then you may be bursting with energy and a burning desire to go for a longer run. Go for it.

## Rediscovering Your Own (Ever-Changing) Pace

*Developing a clear awareness of how we relate to various molds is the key to recovering our authority. For example, as you become aware of such a simple pattern as being trained to sit still in your chair or at your desk, you may find that your body is in fact dictating subtle movements, shifts of weight. You may feel like getting up and walking periodically, or stretching for a couple of moments. As you give more attention to these sensual impulses, you may find that you feel less sluggish, or that your back is less sore at the end of a working day. You may even become dangerously critical of the way in which your work environment is engineered. You may be chided for being too restless.*

-Don Hanlon Johnson

After you've gotten into the groove of running in a more playful and exploratory manner, you may be tempted to count your miles or the amount of time you spend on each run. You may want to set a bar like, x number of miles today, or y number of minutes tomorrow. If you feel so inclined, I recommend you do it, but only as an experiment. What we are testing is whether setting the bar increases or decreases your enthusiasm for running. Try it once and see what happens. If the bar makes you want to avoid running, then lower it or simply remove it altogether. If it makes you more enthusiastic then continue using it or even consider raising it. Again, be experimental in the process.

From my personal experience, counting miles was somewhat self-defeating because I tended set the bar too high, as is the habit of most people trying too hard to succeed. In doing so, it made me not want to run, and when I was running, it made me wish the miles were over and done with. I may have done better to set the bar much lower or not to have one to begin with. Some of my teammates, on the other hand, preferred to plan out how many miles they would run every day and for them it seemed to encourage and excite them rather than take the joy out of the activity as it did for me. Whatever the case may be for you, listen to your desire. It will guide you to the right place.

As a final note on pacing, consider *Fartlek*, the Swedish "innovation" on running that gained mass popularity in the 80s. Fartlek, which means "speed play," is for me simply a derivation of what children do naturally: add variation—whether in pacing or type of movement. Varying the pace and type of movement you perform can allow you to tune into what your body really wants. It means giving yourself the option of slowing down, speeding up, or even stopping and walking at any given moment. Be playful and add other styles of movement such as skipping, doing somersaults, kicking your own bottom, jumping small shrubs, going backward, sideways or in circles, or even dodging imaginary obstacles. Basically, you are allowed to do anything you want, and by granting yourself this freedom, you are likely to discover new ways to do your running—or perhaps more accurately, to be your running. As a result you will avoid the kind of slogging through runs that I experienced in my days of competing. Take note of how you feel after doing (being) your own style of "speed play" (which could well include "slow play"). I recommend you keep a journal just for such observations. You will be surprised to discover that in the process of observing yourself as such you will get to know yourself better and that the positive effects of self-knowledge will ripple into the rest of your life.

# Chapter 16

# Fear

*In our muscles as much as in our ideas, we are trapped by the tyranny of what we come to regard as "normal."*

-Deane Juhan

"Move your legs! Move, damn it!"

Joseph Del Real was a loving, and ultimately demanding, "old-school" coach in the narrow, sweat-filled, basement gym where I was learning to kickbox. He seemed as frustrated with my sudden and seemingly total loss of coordination as I was shocked about it. It was as if, the instant the bell rang, my body suddenly forgot how to move.

The funny thing is I couldn't have followed Joe's simple instructions to save my life—though ironically, it felt like I was indeed, trying to save my life. In real time, I was hardly even conscious of his frantic yelling. It wasn't that I didn't want to listen, but that nothing, except my opponent's fists seemed to penetrate my skull during those terrifying two-minute rounds inside the boxing ring. As a totally inexperienced lightweight, trying to avoid the Goliath fists of an experienced heavyweight (who outweighed me by a hundred pounds) meant an instantaneous loss of all my sense-abilities. It was as if all controls in the proverbial cockpit had suddenly been jammed. From a neurophysiological standpoint, I was in the grips of the startle-reflex.

## The Startle Reflex

We enter the world with one reflex fully intact. It is called the startle reflex and consists of two phases. In phase 1, muscles that straighten your arms and legs, pull your head back and lift your chest, suddenly contract with tremendous force. These muscles are called extensors because they extend your body and pull your body wide open like a starfish. A split second after the start of phase 1, phase 2 begins with the violent contraction of all your flexors—the muscles that pull your body in opposite direction: i.e., inward, in the direction of tight ball. The startle reflex, comprising not only your response to, but your experience of fear, gears you up for either fight or flight. Fear through the startle reflex is a necessary response in the face of real danger and it has allowed our species to survive on the planet. Without fear there would be no human race. With it, however, the human race may be driving itself to extinction.

The startle reflex is itself neutral—that is, neither intrinsically good nor inherently bad—and simply a necessary tool bred into the mammalian nervous system to maximize chances for survival. How we use it or get used by it, however, can determine what kind of lives we lead, and even what kind of society we create. The more triggers that we bind to the startle reflex, the more fearful and anxious we become as individuals. Unfortunately, in a fast-paced society run by high strung individuals, people will tend to associate more and more of the world with fear and anxiety—the latter simply being the fear that things are not going to work out. As a result, things that are not even remotely life threatening will on some level be perceived as such. Getting stuck behind a slow moving car, for example, often to triggers a distinct physiological response, which is based on some (mostly unconscious) level of the fear of being late or perhaps missing out on something important. Being late or missing out are not in and of themselves life threatening, but our hyper-vigilance, clamped jaws, constricted breathing and clenched fingers belie a certain fearfulness that says a hungry lion is ready to pounce. On some deep unconscious level, we are afraid of our own demise when the clock is ticking and the traffic light turns red.

## Lions, Tigers and Bears

From my observation, most of us exhibit some level of hyper-vigilance most of the time. This means that we are unconsciously stuck in a mild to serious state of fight or flight—our responses to everyday life becoming a habitual re-enactment of some portion of the startle reflex, more commonly known as anxiety. And this chronic re-enactment bespeaks an attitude of certainty: we are certain on some (mostly unconscious) level that our life is under constant threat.

When I carry anxiety into the world, I am responding to life as if it were something to be survived. Yet when my life is not truly being threatened, to merely survive is to disrupt my ability to sense and feel. Fear, no matter how small and seemingly inconsequential, is always linked to some increase in muscular tension and consequently, some decrease in control. If I carry anxiety into every day life—meaning that anxiety has become a habit—all of the physiological changes in my body along with the concomitant narrowing of my perception will become the baseline for what I consider to be normal. While this state of dis-ease will color every movement I make, I will remain largely unaware that it could be any other way. I will not realize, in other words, that someone placed sandbags on my shoulders, and that that someone is me.

Such dysfunctional coping has to do with the fact that the same adaptability of the nervous system which allows me to acquire greater sense-ability and thereby produce more fluid and powerful movement also allows me to lose my senses and inadvertently sabotage my movement. Thus, if I carry anxiety for a prolonged period, my nervous system will forget the feeling of freer, more coordinated and powerful movement. And in no longer being able to sense and feel it, I will be unable to replicate it. Recall that being able to move in certain ways means being able to sense and feel how to move in those ways. The less I am able to sense and feel myself, in other words, the less coordinated I become.

The result of all of this is a state of normalcy that feels heavy, ungainly and deadening. In this state of "sensory amnesia," the attendant muscular constriction affects all of my movements thereby requiring more effort to perform even simple tasks such as sitting, standing and walking.* As a result, I will feel a certain heaviness as I go through my days and may even begin to feel helpless or cursed. At some point, I may look to surgeons, God, bad genes, or some other outside source to bear the responsibility for my plight.

## Anxiety: Certainty About Uncertainty

If anxiety is part of my every day existence, it means that I have on some level stereotyped a large portion of life, seeing it through all-or-nothing lenses. The "all" in this case is in the persistence of the anxiety, which I generally carry with me, and which could be manifest as dread, or more likely in a gnawing feeling in the back of my mind that something is not going to work out.

From a movement perspective, stereotyping itself is simply the extinguishing of movement possibilities through the exclusion of a wider array of movement patterns. While this exclusion is most often connected with fear, it is also fundamentally rooted in moving too fast to notice the something between the all and the nothing—or in this case the sometimes between the always and never. Not everything is immediately life-threatening—not even red lights, angry bosses, complaining spouses or surly people at the checkout counter. Unconsciously, however, our stereotyped reactions make us respond as if they were.

Chronic tension and anxiety in the absence of something life-threatening is in other words a form of certainty about the world. It is a certainty that the world is on some level dangerous. And while this is sometimes true, usually it is not. The world is, in fact never static, but rather, constantly fluctuating and uncertain. Yet if I take a fearful, anxiety-ridden posture into the world, I am behaving as if the world were static, and in this case, statically dangerous.

---

* I am borrowing the term "sensory amnesia" from Somatic pioneer, Thomas Hanna.

Looking at it this way, chronic anxiety is a posture which goes hand in hand with my fear of uncertainty. Because it is chronic, and therefore largely fixed, the attitude beneath my fear could be one of certainty that uncertainty is bad and consequently to be avoided. And covering up my fear with aggression, arrogance, or some other mask, does not make me suffer less. Rather, it simply adds a clause to my worldview: the world is dangerous and I can beat it (either with fists, words, complacency or some other form of blocking). In the latter case, I have simply overlain one parasitic posture on top of another, resulting in two constricted postures vying for position within one body.

**To experience how emotions, assumptions and judgment play a role in acture/posture, try the following experiment:**

1. Stand up, or simply sit at the edge of your chair so that your spine is relatively erect. Notice how you are breathing? Which parts of you expand more? Which parts feel heavier or more constricted? How long does the back of your neck feel?
2. What if somebody were standing in the corner of the room looking at you? Notice how this changes your breathing and posture. If you are very attentive, you will notice changes throughout your entire body.
3. What if the person looked at you disapprovingly? Notice how much more this changes your breathing and acture.
4. What if you discovered that the person isn't looking at you, but is actually blind? Can you feel how your breathing suddenly expands again and how much lighter you feel?

# Chapter 17

# Certainty

*I think if we ever reach the point where we think we thoroughly understand who we are and where we came from, we will have failed.*

-Carl Sagan

Our dominant culture is one of being certain. People under its sway (this would be virtually everyone) sometimes recoil at the mere suggestion that there is another way, not realizing that other possibilities exist outside of the one way they have chosen.

I am no exception.

All of us experience absolute certainty when we're sure we're right. During these times our body language, facial expressions and words all confirm that we already have the all answers. I call it the "I know! I know!" attitude, and what it is really expressing is that uncertainty should be avoided.* "I know! I know!" is the compulsive side of certainty which protects our rightness about the world, and thereby makes us feel safe and secure. In the process of locking out the world, however, such absolute "knowing" can prevent new sensations and feelings, and thus, ideas and insights, from entering.

Everybody falls into this trap some of the time. The problem is that many of us fall into it most of the time. Our perception narrows accordingly, and the potential for learning all but disappears. Like the captain of the Titanic, we assume that our way is the best and perhaps only way so we continue barging full steam ahead toward that "harmless" piece of ice.

---

\* As a teacher it might show up as the "What do you mean you don't get it?" attitude.

## Certainty and Perception

In general, certainty keeps me safe and my life relatively stable. It helps me categorize the world such that I know that all apples are red and shiny, and drinking coffee at dusk will keep me up all night. In this manner certainty guides me through daily life without having to think too much and shuttles me toward things I like and away from things I don't like, and which may even be dangerous. Thus, I will happily jump into an expensive car knowing how comfortable the ride will be, but avoid jumping in front of one as it speeds past because I am certain that doing so would lead to injury or death.

There are times, however, when certainty puts us, or others at risk. I may be certain, for example, that driving on the right side of the road is a good idea. Yet if I happen to be in Tokyo instead of Los Angeles, my certainty will likely lead to an accident. I may be certain that the man waving his gun and running toward me is going to shoot me. But what if the man running toward me is actually trying to catch a bus, and his gun upon closer inspection turns out to be a newspaper? This would be problematic if I were a police officer and had already drawn or even fired my weapon.

In all cases, too much certainty is often the major factor in limiting my perception. I literally see, hear, taste, smell and otherwise sense less of what is actually around me when I am too certain. This is because what I see, hear, taste, smell and otherwise sense is strongly colored by what I expect to see, hear, taste, smell and sense. If, for example, apples are supposed to be shiny and red, I may never notice the green ones, which my mind will have unwittingly placed into the "not apple" category.

## The Necessity of Certainty

You could say that certainty begins at birth in the form of the startle reflex: if startled, all newborns will automatically respond with absolute certainty in the manner described earlier. Yet to thrive in the world, our newborn will eventually need to know more than simply how to contract himself into a ball. This is why he is naturally curious and begins exploring the world as soon as he enters it. And as he explores the world, he is simultaneously exploring himself.

As our newborn explores, his mind arranges crude sense-abilities into finer ones. Simple and crude movement patterns thereby become more precise ones. The sum of all of these patterns will eventually become his certain ways of moving and expressing himself. Each level of refinement can be seen as a milestone—a new level of mastery and therefore certainty upon which he can construct ever more refined and complex movements. Once satisfied with crawling, for instance, he will work toward standing and eventually walking.

From this perspective, you could say that certainty is an organized database that keeps our growing infant from having to re-learn the same things over and over again. In this regard certainty allows our newborn to gather, organize and re-organize material. His growing database, which contains emotional, intellectual and movement-based components, comprises the foundation upon which he learns new ways to emote, think and move. His growing database acts, in other words, as a foundation upon which he learns new movement patterns and therefore new behaviors, the collective sum of which could be considered the expression of his being.

## The Necessity of Uncertainty:  Exploring vs. Performing

In the animal kingdom, all action falls under either one of two categories: 1) uncertain, exploratory movement, which is the process of sharpening sense-abilities and thereby learning new movement patterns; or 2) certain, performatory movement, which is the process of utilizing (but not improving) existing sense-abilities, to make use of already mastered skills and acquired movement patterns.

Both exploratory and performatory movements are necessary for survival—the former allowing us to learn, and the latter giving us a way to sidestep learning so that we can perform necessary and independence-giving functions such as walking, talking, putting on clothes, or bringing food to our mouths. In our early years, most of our actions will naturally be of an exploratory nature since we begin life with only crude sense-abilities and therefore virtually no movement patterns in place other than inborn reflexes.

As we get older and continue honing our sense-abilities, we simultaneously acquire more movement patterns and thereby gain more independence. When this occurs, performatory movements begin to take more precedence. By the time we reach adolescence, our movement repertoire will have become so expansive that exploration itself, while still beneficial, will become largely unnecessary. By this point, in other words, most of us will have mastered such an enormous amount of skills that we can to navigate daily life without having to learn anything fundamentally new. Perhaps this is why for many middle school students, every day life will become less about learning and more about repeating old patterns. Adolescence, in other words, is the juncture during which certainty takes over and uncertainty, in the form of exploration, virtually ceases to exist.

To put it more simply, adolescence is when most of us begin to settle into ways of moving and expressing ourselves that we will likely carry into adulthood and perhaps even to the grave. And even though it is considered a time of great freedom and experimentation, the experimenting itself—whether with athletics, art, music, drugs, sex or ideas—often occurs within the confines of basic patterns learned in childhood. Thus, from the perspective of both behavior and learning, adolescence is for many, a time when we begin to live life the way we lived it yesterday. And this means that by the time most of us have settled down into our careers and partnered life, we will have already spent several years doing things the way we have always done them—that is, using the same movement and therefore behavioral habits that we likely acquired in our youth.

## The Power of Uncertainty

*Being creative means being able to relax into uncertainty and confusion.*

-Fritjof Capra

Obviously, there is nothing wrong with doing things the way we have always done them if the way we have always done them works. The problem is that it often doesn't—at least not to the degree that we would like—which brings to light the fact that exploration while unnecessary after a certain age, remains highly useful if we want to continue learning and improving. Exploration is unnecessary, in other words, if we want to continue living the way we are living, but highly useful if we want to learn how to live more fully.

Great athletes, martial artists and dancers are to some degree certain about their movements, but not so certain that they stop exploring and adding new patterns to their "movement database." So even though their movements are efficient, powerful and precise beyond most people's comprehension, they continue to seek a higher level of mastery. They are on some level, uncertain. This is why they are masters.

To test your level of "mastery," go back to Lesson 17 ("Reach & Roll on Your Back") and try it again. After finishing, continue to the next paragraph.

## The Line Between Learning and Getting it Over With

When you attempted the last exploration in Lesson 17, where did you put your foot? After observing hundreds of students over the years, I discovered that the nine out of ten move their foot on a line that is parallel to their midline. It's so uncanny that it's as if I had given the instruction: "Move your foot on a line that is parallel to your midline." That, however, is not the instruction. It's also not not the instruction. What it is is an interpretation of the instruction.

The actual instruction simply asks you to try five different locations for your foot. Any five. If your reaction is to move toward and away from your buttock in a line parallel to your midline you are missing out on a vast number of possibilities. Why? Because rather than confining yourself to a line (Fig 1), you can move your foot in an area (Fig 2).

Moving your foot down a line when you could move it in any direction is needlessly restricting your movement. You can compare it to painting a line straight down the length of a tennis court and then attempting to play a match without stepping off the line. Doing so might be a fun experiment if it is your intention to see what happens under this constraint. But what if every time you played you only stayed on the line, forgetting that you were allowed to step off of it? Without even realizing it, you would be making the game much more difficult and wondering why your opponents always trounced you. You might resign yourself to being a bad tennis player with little hope of improving. You might never realize that your real opponent is not the person across the net.

**Fig.1:** The foot moves downward in a straight line

**Fig.2:** The foot covers a wider area (you have the freedom to move your foot anywhere)

At some time in the future you may choose to go back to Lesson 17 and try it again. If you haven't done so already, see to it that you begin to explore putting your foot off to the side a little. You can even put it in places that you think are outlandish. Be playful about it and in the process of being playful, you will make many discoveries. You will begin to discover foot placements that give you more power to roll your hip. Surprisingly, even discovering less-than-optimal places for your foot will contribute tremendously to your learning.

As a final note, I think of facing uncertainty as opening the door for new possibilities to emerge. We may not always welcome uncertainty (I rarely do), and we may face it with some level of trepidation (I almost always do), but simply facing the unknown often creates openings where none previously existed.

# Epilogue

# The Rest of Your Life (Definitely skip this part if you haven't slowed down yet)

*When you are wholehearted about something… when you are where you want to be and are participating fully in the moment you are in—sometimes enthusiastic, sometimes mellow—you will experience a new sense of aliveness. You will experience a surge of energy, renewed vigor. This is not because there is actually an increase in energy, but because you are not constricting it quite so much. There is now a better energy flow. There is less conflict, less friction, less not wanting to be where you are, and therefore—for you—there will be the experience of more energy.*

*This occurs when you are not trying to spin clockwise and counterclockwise simultaneously. Spinning in opposite directions happens when you act on opposing desires, when you are conflicted about what you are doing, not wholehearted—granted, this is most of the time.*

-Erich Schiffmann

Fifteen years since my introduction to Feldenkrais and Chinese martial arts I find myself ever more experimental with and intrigued by movement. When I think about how much better I feel in middle age than I did in the supposed prime of my life—during which I was too busy hurrying to be interested in paying attention and exploring—I know that slowing down has fundamentally altered my being. It's not just that I move with much more awareness than when I was younger, but moreover, that I perceive more of myself and therefore, more of life now that I tune into my senses.

Contrary to my experience in school and organized sports—both of which tended to encourage mimicry, imitation and rote—Feldenkrais, Bagua and Taichi led me to tune in and come to my senses. The crucial element of slowing down to enhance sense-ability has reintroduced curiosity, wonder and learning into my life, and subsequently turned my bodymind into an exciting laboratory through which I am continuously making important discoveries. After one of my early immersion periods into Bagua and Feldenkrais, for example, I began to experience the joy of walking for the first time. Where walking, like everything else in my life, had once been a chore to be gotten over with, it had suddenly become a process to be enjoyed through entirely new sense-abilities—ones that made my gait light, fluid and powerful. Walking for miles through the streets of New York City after having just returned from my first summer with Master Ge and Master Li, I remember feeling vibrant and playful, like a child who has just been given a new toy.

By the end of my second summer with the masters, I was stronger, faster and more grounded than ever, even though I didn't lift weights and hadn't run a step in ten years. Bagua and Feldenkrais were helping me develop a deeper connection with my own body, far beyond anything I had ever experienced during my days of competitive racing. Confident that it would show in my running, I jumped into a 10K road race as an afterthought and placed third in my age group—one that seemed to include an inordinate number of balding fathers who were apparently in the habit of eating too many dinner rolls. Though placing well among overweight, middle-aged dads wasn't exactly earth shattering, what astonished me was the fact that my stride felt much freer and more powerful than it did when, well over a decade prior, I was running five to ten miles a day. This feeling would become more obvious weeks later while visiting a friend in Toronto.

When I arrived at my friend's house, situated in an old Slavic section of the city, we decided to walk down the street to a neighborhood restaurant. Two years of immersion learning had resulted in my gait becoming fluid and smooth, while my chest felt as if it were floating upward, rather than weighing me down as it had for most of my life. My head was literally higher and my gaze less downward than just a couple years previous—not because I was trying to hold everything up, but because through all the exploring I had done, my skull had naturally gravitated to a new, more comfortable position. The ease and comfort I felt, a natural result of more deeply sensing myself, allowed me to take in more of my environment. In contrast to much of the way I had been surviving most of my life by unconsciously tuning out of it, I felt much more at peace and tuned in to everything around me. I can still remember the red brick row houses, the overcast sky at dusk, the brightly lit health food store that we stopped at on the way, and the sound of what could have been Polish spoken by two elderly women as they strolled past us.

Perhaps the only thing I wasn't tuned into was where I had left my wallet.

Upon reaching the restaurant, I realized that I had forgotten it back at the house. Knowing that my friend wouldn't mind waiting the few minutes it would take for me to make the round trip, I turned around and began striding back in an easy and relaxed manner. The funny thing is that no longer in a hurry (or for that matter, trying to beat out the nearest overweight, middle-aged dad), I felt faster and lighter than ever. In fact, my stride felt so effortless and strangely powerful that it was as if I were gliding on air. Right then and there, for the first time in my life, I had a real sense of how great runners must feel as they glide down the track. By this, I don't mean that I had suddenly reached an Olympic caliber, but rather that I could finally relate to the effortless power I had witnessed in so many great runners. Try as I had during my track days, I could never come close to imitating the runners that I so admired. I couldn't imitate them because I had never slowed down enough to accurately sense what I was doing and consequently had no sense of what they were doing. During these moments of effortless striding, however, I felt at along last like I was in on their secret. And it took not trying to run fast to really notice how fast I had become.

As I continued easily down the street, I knew I was finally not only on the road to being a better runner, but one to freedom. Over ten years removed from running and without the slightest interest in returning to competition, I had become faster and than I ever imagined was possible. The unmistakable feeling of power and freedom had finally arrived because I had finally stopped trying to be.

## "Side" Benefits

For those of you who have made time to explore the lessons in this book, you may have discovered over the course of weeks or months that along with running better, other aspects of your life have started to change. For example, you may have noticed positive changes in your acture—which, perhaps, you no longer think of as posture—improvements in your ability to perform other sports, and greater ease in performing every day activities such as walking, mowing the lawn or even doing the dishes.

How could all of this be possible just from having slowed down?

Your nervous system is remarkable in its ability to integrate deepened sense-ability into all of your movements so that even though you may have set out to improve your running, other movements have improved as well. This is why performing other activities may have become more interesting and even pleasurable. Your sleep may have become deeper and more restful as your increased sense-ability has decreased residual tension, thereby allowing your chest cavity and abdomen to become more expansive and your back and shoulders to let go. You may gradually become more aware of how you move through your days and be able to feel subtler tensions in your body well before they build up into something like a backache, headache or sore shoulders. You may find yourself more able to let go.

# Holding onto Life is Not the Same as Living It

*A chronic muscular contraction is not something that somebody else is doing to me. It is something that I am doing to myself.*

-Stanley Keleman

Letting go can be scary. Holding on feels comparatively safe. Perhaps there is something biological about it: grasping is one of the first natural reflexes that a newborn infant displays. She holds on firmly to her mother.

Yet growing up means letting go of mom and many other things. We must periodically let go because holding itself prevents us from grasping anything new.

People and objects are not the only things that we hold onto. Holding is also written into our habitual movement patterns and these patterns constrain to a large degree how we deal with life. With this in consideration, it is of enormous benefit to acquire new movement patterns that give us more freedom in how we choose to encounter and move through the world—patterns that allow us to let go of stress rather than cling to it.

If, for example, in the process of slow exploration I learn ways of breathing and moving about that are less restrictive and less laden with tension, I will be starting from a calmer and more confident place to begin with. I might, for example, begin to literally feel how particular parts of my ribcage are able to move and expand, allowing more breath to flow through me. I may notice a softening in the deep muscles of my lower belly that not only releases tension, but allows for a greater exchange of gasses and fluids through my tissues and internal organs. I might discover ways to move my spine that relieve the muscles in my shoulders and the back of my neck. Embodying these new movement patterns I will begin to move, and therefore respond differently, possibly facing the world with less anxiety and fear.

Dealing with life's downs, however, is not the only or most important benefit of letting go. For life is not only about coping with the unexpected, the unpleasant, and the tragic. It is also about feeling pleasure, joy and wonder. Consider that excessive holding has a two-fold effect: it makes me more anxious and fearful in times of increased stress, and it makes me less able to feel pleasure, peace and joy in times when I am not faced with difficulties.

We can only become aware of pleasure and feelings like joy and peace through our senses. If we totally lacked sense-ability, pain and fear would no longer dog us. But then again, pleasure and love would not exist. Looking at it this way, pain and fear are not evils to be extinguished, but a necessary part of life to be dealt with sensibly. By being able to sense and feel more, you do just that: create the possibility for a sense-able rather than sense-less response. Moreover, you simultaneously allow yourself to truly experience pleasure and joy. Improving your sense-ability, then, not only allows you to better deal with stress, but it gives you the opportunity to more fully experience what it means to be alive.

## When "Normal" Means Abnormal

*[T]he 'normal' life that most humans lead is a life of unconscious self-destruction. If they were conscious of it, they would not do this to themselves, but as it is, they have no choice. They are hapless victims of a society in which a regular and insupportable burden of stress is consciously accepted as normal while, unconsciously, the central nervous system is brutalized to the point that it can no longer sustain the burden.*

-Thomas Hanna

As we saw in Chapter 7 ("To Be or Not To Be"), movement and response-ability are both colored by sense-ability: the less I can sense and feel myself, the fewer options I will have in both responding to the world and expressing that response. Hurrying and forcing, for example, express themselves through the constriction of muscles in my spine, ribcage, abdomen and pelvis such that my breathing automatically becomes more shallow. Hurrying as a habit consequently leads my normal state to be one of constriction and reduced oxygenation, not because I consciously choose it, but because my mind has forgotten how to let go of and expand all of the tissue surrounding my lungs. Thus, if I compulsively hurry and force my way through daily life, I will over time literally lose the sense of what it feels like not to hurry and force. Through habituation, in other words, the neural pathways that allow for a fuller movement of my entire ribcage, spine and pelvic basin will have been pruned away. As a result, I will have fewer resources for staying calm, more likely acting with some measure of anxiety and frustration when faced with stress. In the extreme, I may even withdraw or explode under the mildest of adverse conditions. Whether I close down timidly, strike out angrily, or simply clench my jaw and bear it, I will feel stuck with the situation not realizing that what I am really stuck with is a limited number of ways of both perceiving and expressing myself.

Stress can be a powerful learning tool if, rather than looking at the stressor in isolation, we examine our response to it. From this perspective, stress can be seen as something that we inadvertently accumulate when we don't know how to release it from our bodies and minds. Thus, how I react to whatever new befalls me depends crucially on how much stress I have accumulated to begin with. If, for example, I am typically a shallow breather, or tend to grip hard on the steering wheel, or suck my belly in tightly, or clench my jaw, I will not have at my easy disposal deeper ways of breathing or moving about my world that would allow me to handle any added stress with a measure of calm. And the crux here is not simply that I deal poorly with added stress, but that I am already stressed-out to begin with—even before the outside world intervenes. The sense-abilities that I'm habitually locked into, in other words, are ones that keep my normal level of tension and discomfort at a higher level.

The irony here is that my normal everyday state undermines my own well-being. I do not maintain such "normalcy" to intentionally harm myself or those around me, but rather as a matter of habit and familiarity. Significant here is the fact that not only are certain muscles perpetually clenching and holding on, but that the mind to which they are attached is telling them to do so. It is as if I am saying to myself, "Hold on, or else!"

## Or Else What?

*A bit of advice*
*given to a young Native American*
*at the time of his initiation:*
*As you go the way of life,*
*you will see a great chasm.*
*Jump.*
*It is not as wide as you think.*

-Joseph Campbell

"Or else what?" is a question that cannot be easily answered. And perhaps this is why it is so common in our culture to live with fear and certainty. We are certain that the unknown is something to be avoided so we hold on to what is familiar. But holding on is not really living. And were it possible, knowing the unknown before it arrived would make life rather uninteresting.

Life is uncertain and by trying to evade uncertainty, we are evading life. Perhaps this is why clinging to certainty can be so disruptive to our ability to feel pleasure. For we cannot extinguish pain from our lives without simultaneously extinguishing pleasure. We cannot anaesthetize ourselves with painkillers, video games, TV or the latest gadget and at the same time feel more deeply. Sensing more in our bodies and our hearts requires that we turn down the volume of extraneous inputs so that we can begin notice the whispers of wind blowing, allow new sensations to enter our bodies, hear the voices deep within ourselves.

At the extreme, certainty imprisons us like royalty high up in our castles (or, if you prefer, politicians in the Capitol) and prevents us from truly seeing and knowing others. Safely behind our moat, we can view maps of the world, look at photographs of it, or even watch TV programs that simulate it. Yet from this distance we are not really part of the map making or the picture taking or indeed, the living. Our certainty, in other words, which resides in our thoughts, sets us apart from the world, which rests in our bodies through our sensing and feeling. As our sense-abilities consequently shrivel, we lose touch with the world itself. Rather than experiencing life directly, we filter it through our "I know! I know!" attitude, trading compassion and understanding for defensiveness, wonder for being right, living for surviving.

Perhaps the greatest loss in this process of desensitization is the fact that we have turned against ourselves. Certainty in the form of "shoulds" and "shouldn'ts," otherwise known as self-judgment, limits our ways of moving, behaving and expressing ourselves. We become a stereotype of ourselves rather than being ourselves. For it is precisely because we think we know ourselves that we are no longer in touch with our sensing and feeling—or in other words, who we really are. Because we are not good enough, we try to be something that we are not. Rather than being, we turn to not being.

We have, in other words, become human not beings living within highly regulated modes of thought and behavior that are circumscribed by perpetual certainty, otherwise known as the all-or-nothing, otherwise known as fear.

What are we afraid of?

The answer is right in front of our noses: we are struggling so hard to not be because we are in fact afraid of being. And we are afraid because the act of being, which is simply sensing and feeling more deeply and therefore living life more fully, carries no guarantees.

## Not Quite Living

Many of us exert a great deal of effort trying to get the present moment out of the way. Whether the moment involves driving to work, work itself, exercising, spending time with a loved-one or friend, eating, or even having sex, we are often not quite here, but rather trying to get to the next moment before the present one is fully felt in our bodies. Indeed, we rarely experience the present because we are racing so quickly toward the future. And we are racing because we are mired in the past, believing that what befalls us in the present has already been experienced before. Our certainty about the present moment has become a sort of "been there, done that" attitude slavishly driving us toward something less predictable and more stimulating—something, in a word, new.

Boredom, which has become epidemic in modern society, must be conquered with the newest video games (notice how anything more than a few years old is no longer worth playing), TV, the internet, snacking, amusement parks, or other forms of non-interactive, passive entertainment. Chronic pain, which has become so widespread as to become a medical condition in and of itself rather than just a symptom, must be quickly subdued with drugs. Deep felt pleasure, which is so absent as to have entire industries devoted to simulating it, has come to be replaced by cheap imitations (which are actually quite expensive when you think about it) that assault our taste buds, over stimulate our glands, dull our minds and eventually leave us in despair. What we want is for life to be more stimulating, pleasurable and exciting and therefore less predictable, painful and boring. What we get is the opposite: more predictability, pain and boredom.

The irony in all this is that nothing about life is predictable or boring— except that is, when we are not present to experience the something between the all and the nothing. By trying to make life less predictable, painful and boring, however, we simply do the opposite. Perhaps herein lies the message that life is giving us: we cannot improve life by avoiding it; we cannot to infuse life with what we think is more life, and not end up subduing it.

## Sense-ability and Freedom

> *There was a group of students who would occasionally bring Professor flowers to see him practice his love of flower arranging. I have no sense of how good he was at it; his arrangements were beautiful, but the formal art of flower arranging is beyond my understanding. I was always awed, though, watching a man of his great power displaying utter delicacy as he trimmed and shaped his floral arrangements. His delicacy resonated in that gentle place in me that I had blocked off for my adult life because I feared it wasn't manly. One of the many gifts he gave me was the way he led me back to the best part of myself.*

> -Wolfe Lowenthal on Master Cheng Man Ch'ing

Sensing and feeling are the filters through which life enters. By choosing how much we are willing to sense and feel, we are actually choosing how much of life to let in at any given moment. Life simply is, and moment-to-moment we are determining what fraction of it is gets in.

In the end, what increasing sense-ability lends us is greater discerning power over what we let in and what we don't. We literally have more choices and therefore more freedom when we are able to sense more of the something between the all-or-nothing. Increasing sense-ability, in other words, allows us to more precisely determine what is at each moment so that we have more choice in the matter. Decreasing sense-ability, on the other hand, blocks out more of what is so that we have less choice. Of course, this doesn't mean we should never block things out, but rather that most of our blocking is actually unconscious and thus, limiting. I may consciously choose to put in earplugs before attending a rock concert, for example, but (unconsciously) forget that they are in after leaving the concert. By putting in the earplugs, I am exercising choice. By forgetting that they are in, however, I am losing the choice of hearing my surroundings.

Unconscious habits are where we remain deaf to what is because we have forgotten to take out the earplugs. If, for example, I can't clearly feel how my ribcage moves with each step I take, I am not only deaf to certain movements in my own body, but unaware of how to use the movements in order to generate more power. Unable to clearly sense my own movements, in other words, I automatically move with less control over and hence, less power in my stride. I may think I am free, yet if I ignore the option of improving my sense-ability, the only remaining option is to try harder in order to improve.

Here is where I am faced with a critical choice: I can act with certainty by hurrying up and trying harder, or I can slow down and simply allow myself to be. In the former case, I reduce my sense-ability, increase my "deafness" and consequently reinforce my habitual movement patterns. In the latter, I take out the proverbial earplugs, increase my "hearing" and move outside the realm of habit.

In this sense, running faster is a choice, though not the one most people believe it to be.

But getting myself to run faster is not why I began slowing down. And getting you to run faster is not why I wrote this book.

# Appendix I

# The Feldenkrais Method

The Feldenkrais Method was born out of a childlike curiosity that all of us possess. Its founder, Dr. Moshe Feldenkrais, exemplified the same fiercely independent way of thinking that we see in all great scientists, musicians, artists, writers, dancers and athletes—indeed, anyone who values exploration, uncertainty and playfulness. It is also the same sort of mindset that we see in infants, toddlers and young children and that we ourselves embody in our more spontaneous, less defensive and perhaps more vulnerable moments.

Born in Ukraine in 1904, Feldenkrais traveled on foot and alone to what is now Israel at the age of thirteen. Several years later he attended the Sorbonne in Paris and begin working toward his doctorate in Mechanical Engineering under Frederic Joliot-Curie, the 1935 Nobel Prize winner in chemistry. While at the Sorbonne, Feldenkrais met Jigoro Kano, the distinguished Japanese physicist and founder of Judo.

At its highest levels judo remains an art dominated by the "soft," or other words, those most persistent in listening. In this regard, judo, which means, "the soft way," can be considered the art of cultivating sense-ability. Robert W. Smith writes, "Kano envisaged judo as an educative process for the masses of all countries…"

> *He developed this into a system of physical and ethical education. His strategy embraced two ideas: 1) maximum efficiency with minimum effort, and 2) mutual welfare. We have forgotten that the first*

*maxim covered life as well as sport judo and few of us seem to have*
*ever learned the meaning of the second (which means simply love).*

-Robert W. Smith

After meeting Kano, Feldenkrais, a high level martial artist himself, im-
mersed himself in the study of judo, and quickly rose in the European ranks.
Seeing judo's vast potential to further growth and human development he later
wrote several important books on the art. Human development through exploring movement, or what he called, "awareness through movement," was to become
a major theme in Dr. Feldenkrais' later work.

# Appendix II

## The Lessons

# Things to keep in mind...

*"If you hit a million balls against a backboard, and are inattentive or bored, your arm may grow stronger, but your awareness won't, and little will be learned; in fact, you may not even recognize that you're bored and playing a game you don't enjoy."*

– W. Timothy Gallwey, *Inner Tennis*

## Go Slowly

Unless otherwise instructed, go slowly so that you can be more attentive and feel what is happening in your body. Change your pace from time to time. Go a little slower, or a little faster and notice how it affects the precision in your movement.

## No Pain = More Gain

Stop if anything hurts or if you feel like you are straining. Learning occurs much faster when you are not distracted by discomfort and can give your full attention to what you are doing. Doing anything without your full attention, on the other hand, generally stifles learning. Straining or pushing to the point of discomfort in any capacity—whether physical or emotional—tends to block your mind from getting new information. Some lessons, such as ones from the "Throwing the Ball" series, will be challenging at first, leading certain muscles to tire quickly. I recommend you not push yourself during these lessons because your precision will suffer as a result. As I have suggested many times in this book, you get more out of things when you stop trying to get more out of them.

## Notice if You Feel Bored or Frustrated

Going with the "No Pain, More Gain" approach, stop if at any point you frustrated or even bored. You are better off resting or even doing something else if you feel any of these. Discomfort, strain, frustration and boredom are the greatest saboteurs of learning.

## Rest Frequently

Don't wait until you are tired before stopping. It isn't the number of repetitions you perform that matters, but whether you are becoming more precise in your ability to sense your own movement. Improving precision depends crucially on resting periodically.

## Savor New Sensations... Do a Body Scan

Scan yourself before and after each lesson (and if you want, during rest periods). This way you will start to notice subtle changes in your body. These changes are an indication of neurological change also known as learning. They are what will guide you to more power, speed, agility and fluidity. Furthermore, they will enhance your enjoyment.

## Be Playful

After you've completed an entire lesson, it isn't necessary to start from the beginning. Feel free to skip around. Whatever step in the lesson you go to, the key is to be attentive, playful and exploratory.

## Close Your Eyes

For lessons where you are lying down or sitting, I recommend keeping your eyes closed unless otherwise directed. Closing your eyes tends to diffuse your focus and thereby free up your neck muscles. It also helps you to direct your attention to what you are sensing and feeling. For standing lessons, I recommend keeping your eyes open, unless otherwise instructed.

## Work With Friends

I encourage you work with a partner or group of friends. Take turns reading lessons to each other and exploring them together—perhaps before and/or after running together.

# Lessons 1-8

# "Throwing the Ball" Series

The "Throwing the Ball" series will help you develop particular movement patterns used by Bagua adepts as well as professional athletes. The starting positions may seem unusual and challenging at first since these lessons are designed to awaken areas in your body that have been dormant for years and possibly decades. As your body awakens and your sense-ability increases, what was at first challenging will quickly become easier. The reason is that rather than simply working harder at habitual movements, you will be working smarter by exploring novel movements.

Each of the lessons is designed to build power through coordination, which is why it is possible to feel to significant improvements in both posture and propulsive force in a short period of time. Devoting 20-30 minutes every day to "Throwing the Ball" lessons, can lead to significant changes by the end of the week. By the seventh day, what once seemed very difficult will likely seem manageable and probably much easier. Of course consistency in exploring lessons over a longer period of time—say a month to six months—will lead to far greater improvements.

Finally, for all the lessons that involve standing, I recommend using a full-length mirror to check both your beginning and ending positions. The mirror can help you become aware of what you wouldn't otherwise notice, such as when you start leaning forward or bending sideways. Videotaping can be even more powerful because it allows you to see even more of what you wouldn't otherwise notice about your own movement.

## Lesson 1

# Throwing the Ball 1:  Posing Questions

**Starting Position:** Take off your shoes and place an imaginary baseball in your right hand (even if you are left-handed) and begin throwing it.

1.  Do this a few times in slow motion as if you wanted to throw with speed and accuracy (if you've played baseball, imagine throwing from third base to first). How much power do you have? If you haven't done so already, make sure that you are throwing with your left foot in front.

2.  Begin to freeze at the very end of your throw and notice how much balance you have. How long could stand this way without toppling? How relaxed is your right shoulder? Which way is your left foot pointing? Straight? At an angle to the left? At an angle to the right? Where is your left knee relative to your left ankle?

People encountering this lesson for the first time will usually lean forward with their upper body, believing that this will afford them more power. They will tend to strain their right shoulder unconsciously, by lifting it unnecessarily. And they will allow their left knee to go so far forward that it reaches past their toes. Any one of these is an indication that they are not maximizing their power. Fur-

Which one looks like the most comfortable way of throwing?

thermore, this way of using the knee and shoulder could eventually lead to injury.

3. Here we arrive at some basic questions:

    How can you perform the action without leaning forward?

    How can you perform it without your left knee going forward, yet still gain power?

    Is it possible to throw the ball without moving your head, so that your it stays in exactly the same place through the entire motion—neither moving forward, backward, up, down or to either side?

    What would happen if your left knee moved backward (without straightening) as your right hand moved forward?

4. It can be gratifying to seek answers to questions like the ones I posed above. In just a few minutes, the seeking can reveal a tremendous amount. From a neuro-physiological standpoint, the seeking actually creates new neural pathways—as long as I go slowly enough and pay close attention to the sensations in my body. For me, seeking answers is like deciphering the meaning of a good poem or the lyrics to a well-written song. Each time I return to a lesson—some of which I have explored an untold number of times—I discover something new. Each time, I feel tension releasing in a matter of seconds.

5. Take a break for as long as you want to ponder the questions—seconds, minutes, or hours—then, try this lesson again. Repeat this lesson as many times as you like and then proceed to Lesson 2.

# Lesson 2

# Throwing the Ball 2: The Power of Your 1st Metatarsal

**Starting Position 1:** Return to throwing the imaginary baseball with your right hand in standing. Remember to have your left foot forward. Repeat a few times to see what it feels like—it is quite likely that the previous lessons have had a lasting impact. Pause.

**Starting Position 2:** Drop your arms and place your right foot about twelve inches to the right of your midline (the imaginary line that divides your right and left sides).

1.   (Leaving your arms down) imagine there is a smoldering cigarette under the ball of your right foot. Begin to crush out the cigarette by rotating on the ball of your right foot. Notice how you rotate: your knee will move and possibly your right hip as well. It's possible other parts of you will also rotate. Which part(s) of the

ball of your foot are you rotating on? Specifically, which metatarsals make contact with the floor? Pause.

2. Go back to crushing out the cigarette, but this time make sure that you do so only with the 1st metatarsal joint (you must keep the outside edge of your foot high in the air and lift your toes at the same time). Notice how far your foot rotates in each direction. Most people will rotate more externally, sweeping their right knee further and further to the right. Explore this movement, going back and forth a few times slowly before resting. In resting, notice which leg feels longer and more rooted into the floor.

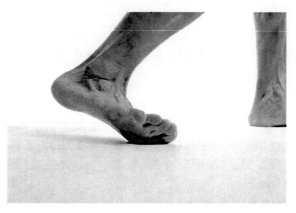

3. Come back to the previous position with your left foot forward. Turn your right knee to the left so that it points at your left knee. Now draw your right knee toward your left leg until it touches the back of your left knee. The top of your right thigh should be touching the inside of your left thigh.

    a. Again, allow only the 1st metatarsal joint of your right foot to make contact with the floor. Begin to crush the cigarette by externally rotating your right leg. Your right knee will begin sweeping to the right.

    b. Go back and forth very slowly, staying on your 1st metatarsal joint. With each iteration, the top of your right thigh should return to making contact with the inside of your left thigh. Notice how much work your legs have to do! You are beginning to tap into something major league pitchers, World Cup soccer players, NBA point guards, and professional tennis players do naturally: fully use the strongest muscles in their body to generate power.

4. Rest, noticing the difference between the two sides of your body—particularly your legs. Walk around and notice how much more power you have as you push off your right foot.

5. Repeat steps 1-4 on the other side.

# Lesson 3

# Throwing the Ball 3: Discovering Power in Your Hips in Sidelying

**Starting Position:** Lie down on your left side with your left foot resting on the floor—the entire sole against the wall. If you need support under your head, fold bath towels neatly and stack them under your left cheek. Make sure that your left foot is far enough forward so that you can see your ankle (your left knee will be bent). Reach down with your fingers and locate the joint that connects your right big toe to the ball of your foot. We'll call this the 1st metatarsal joint. Squeeze it firmly from both the top and the bottom so that you can feel it clearly and then let go and rest your right hand on top of your left hand (as shown in the figure below). Place your right foot on the wall about one foot behind your body and about two feet off the floor. Lift your heel and the outside edge of your foot so that only the 1st metatarsal joint of your foot is touching the wall. Lift all of your toes so that except for your big toe, none are in contact with the wall.

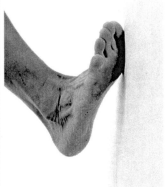

1. Begin to rotate as if to crush out a cigarette again. Notice how your right hip moves as you do this. Go back and forth slowly a few times. Be very observant of keeping everything but the 1st metatarsal joint off the wall. Notice when the

outside edge of your right foot starts to drop such that the 2nd or 3rd metatarsal joints begin to touch the wall.

2.  Now rotate further forward and notice what prevents you from going further. Again, be vigilant that the outside edge of your right foot and everything but your 1st metatarsal and big toe stay away from the wall. Repeat a few times, then pause.

3.  Now as you crush out the cigarette see to it that your right side of your pelvis rolls forward at the same time. Allow the right side of your pelvis and your right foot rotate in synchrony. Repeat a few times, each time noticing when the foot and pelvis are out of sync. Rest on your back.

4.  Return to the same configuration and this time as you rotate your foot and pelvis, simultaneously turn your head to look to your left—that is, toward the floor. See to it that you move your head more and more in synchrony with the movement of your leg. Go slowly enough so that you notice when your head begins to move faster than your leg or your leg faster than your head. Repeat this a few times and rest on your back.

5.  In resting, notice if you feel like half of your body is sinking more into the floor, or if the floor is tilting to one side. This is an indication that muscles on half of you have given up a lot of their extraneous tension.

6.  Come back to the same configuration and this time place your right hand on the floor just in front of your left hand. Begin to slide it away from you as if trying to reach something on the floor just beyond your fingertips. Start with a very small, slow movement.

    As you slide forward notice if your leg moves as well. Notice when other parts of your foot start to make contact with the wall—again, only the big toe and 1st metatarsal joint should to be in contact with the wall.

    Close your eyes and allow your head to roll on the floor as you reach forward. This should feel very good since it releases the muscles in your neck (as long as you go slowly). As your body gets more in sync, everything from head to toe will literally move at the same time. Repeat this a few times.

Now try leading once with your right foot to see if your leg, hand and arm follow. Keep your eyes closed. Is your head rolling easily on the floor?

Try leading once by gently rolling your head to see if your hand and leg follow. Alternate between leading with your head, hand and foot, each time checking to see if the other parts of you are moving in synchrony.

Rest on your back and notice if the two sides of your body feel even more different than before (perhaps one side is sinking even more).

7. Repeat steps 1-6 on the other side. Each time you rest, notice if the other side of your body is sinking more into the floor.

8. When you are finished, take your time to stand up and notice if your neck feels longer and if your shoulders have dropped their tension. Your legs may feel more grounded. Walk around and notice if your hips free looser and if you have more power in pushing off the balls of your feet.

Note that some people have sensitivities in their 1st metatarsal joint. As a variation, you can use the 2nd metatarsal joint, or the area between the 1st and the 2nd joint.

## Lesson 4

# Throwing the Ball 4:  Stabilizing Your Front Leg While Lying Down

**Starting Position:** Lie on your back with your rear end about 1 foot from a wall—close enough that you can place the sole of your left foot against it with your left knee bent. Comfortably fold your right leg underneath—let it rest so that your right foot is somewhere between your right buttock and the wall and your knee is turned out to the right (place cushions under your right knee if you feel any pulling in your groin muscles).

1. In this position, bring your left foot as close to the floor as possible while keeping the toes pointing toward the ceiling. The closer you come to the floor, the more your heel will lift.

2. Pretend that the wall is a garage door that slides up and down. Begin to push your left foot into this door in as if you wanted to slide it up (This lesson is better to do without socks so that your foot doesn't slide). Push with gradually increasing force and then release just as slowly. Repeat a few times. Notice which muscles in your leg begin to work. Notice if there is there a strain in your left knee. How much power do you have in raising the garage door? What effect is there on your left hip?  Do you feel movement in your spine?

3. Slide your foot 3 inches higher and repeat. Your heel should be closer to the wall

now if it isn't already touching it. Do you get more comfort and power in this position or the previous one with your foot closer to the floor?

4. Slide your foot another 3 inches higher and repeat. Notice how the higher you place your foot on the wall, the more pressure you exert with your heel and the power you get.* Notice how your hips and spine are affected differently as you place your foot higher.

5. Continue placing your foot higher up the ceiling and "sliding" the garage door. At some height, you will begin to lose power. What height is that? Rest.

   Each height simulates a different way to use your front leg when throwing a ball, or reversing/changing directions (as tennis and soccer players often do). When your knee is bent too far, you lose power and compromise stability in your knee. When your heel is raised, it forces your calf muscles to do more work. (for more on this go to Chapter 14 ("Running Shoes").

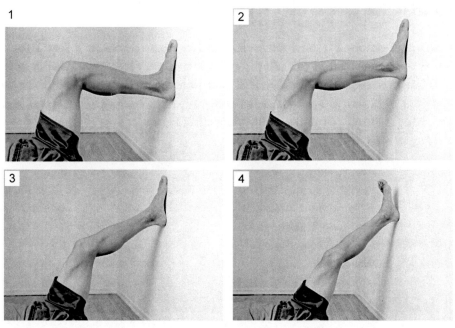

Steps 3 - 5

6. Return to the same configuration and continue exploring where you can get more power in sliding the garage door. Here are some possible explorations:

   a. Turn your foot out 25 degrees and see how pushing this way affects your ankle, knee and hip differently. Even your spine will be affected. Repeat a few times.

---

* Because the heel is higher than midsole in the vast majority of shoes, most peoples' calf muscles are overworked, short and tight. This lesson will help to lengthen the calf muscles and activate other areas in your legs to help produce more power and balance while stabilizing your knees.

b.  Turn your foot out 45 degrees and continue, observing the effects. Repeat a few times.

c.  Place your foot so that the toes point directly at the ceiling. Repeat a few times as you compare the effects.

d.  Turn your foot in 25 degrees and compare the effects.

e.  Turn your foot in 45 degrees and compare. After repeating a few times, rest. Each different angle for your foot will have a marked effect on how you use not only your left leg, but your entire body. As you probably observed, you gain more or less power depending on the direction your toes point. Your knee also feels more or less stable, depending on the direction. Turning your foot outward tends to result in less power and more undue torsion on your knee. Yet many people walk and run in this fashion due to muscle imbalances throughout their legs and pelvis

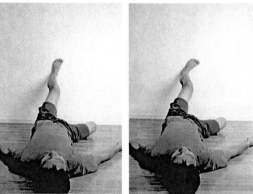

Steps 6.a - 6.e

7.  Repeat each step on the other side. When you are finished, stand up and throw an imaginary ball a few times, noticing how you use your front leg. Walk and notice how your walking has changed.

# Lesson 5

# Throwing the Ball 5: Stabilizing Your Front Leg While Sitting

**Starting Position:** Sit on the right corner of a sturdy chair such that your left foot points directly forward and your right leg is a little behind you and out to the side.* Your right leg should be far enough behind and such that your heel is off the floor. Make sure you are sitting comfortably tall in the chair (i.e. neither slouched nor stiff like a drill sergeant).

  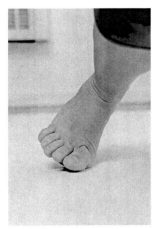

1.  Begin to push back with your left leg as if you wanted to slide the chair backward.
2.  Just as in Lesson 4 notice how the placement of your foot as well as the angle in which it's pointing influences both power and comfort.
3.  What's happening in your right hip and leg? Begin to rotate on the 1st metatarsal joint of your right foot as you push back with your left foot. Your hips should swivel on the chair, bringing your right hip forward and left hip backward. Notice how your right knee begins to turn inward and down toward the ground. Go

---

* Note that a high stool works better if you have long legs (You may want to try one if you are 5'6" or taller).

back and forth several times feeling how your hips rotate in relation to the pushing of your left foot and the rotation of the right foot. Rest.

4. Experiment with placing your left foot in different locations on the floor (i.e., further forward, backward, right and left). Also try turning it in different directions. Just as in Lesson 4, see how each placement and direction affects the movement. When done experimenting with your left foot, begin to experiment with placing your right foot in different locations and notice how this affects the movement. Rest.

5. Stand up and feel the difference between the two sides of your body. Throw the imaginary ball with your right hand and pay attention to the placement of your feet. See if you can stay on the first metatarsal of your right foot.

6. Walk around and feel the difference in the push-off of the two feet.

7. Repeat each step on the other side.

# Lesson 6

# Throwing the Ball 6:  Stabilizing Your Front Leg in Standing

## Stabilizing and Elongating Your Spine

**Starting Position:**  Return to standing and begin to simulate throwing the imaginary baseball with your right hand. Remember to have your left foot forward and this time place your right foot 12 inches to the right of your midline (the line dividing your right and left sides). Now leave your arms resting at your sides. See if you can stay on the 1st metatarsal of the right foot.*

Notice the stability in the
legs and spine

1.   Rotate your hips and crush out the imaginary cigarette under your 1st metatarsal joint. Go back and forth each time rotating more to the left—that is, turning your entire pelvis to the left. When you reach full rotation to the left, pause and

---

* Again, if you have sensitivities in your first metatarsal joint, explore the lesson on the 2nd metatarsal or somewhere between the 1st and the 2nd. Even if you don't have sensitivities, it can be very helpful to explore rotating on other parts of the ball of your foot.

notice if you can still see your left ankle. If not, push your left hip backward: this action will automatically pull your left knee backward.

2. Exploring the movement with these constraints will make your legs work much more. Doing it this way will begin will more fully activate your gluteal muscles as well as your quadriceps. Notice if you are leaning forward. Most people will unconsciously lean forward as they perform this movement, not realizing that by doing so they are throwing themselves off balance and losing power at the same time.

3. Finally, see if you can sink your chest back and downward almost as if to slouch—

Notice the *lack* of stability
in each of these examples

in order to keep your upper body directly over your pelvis. The sinking of your chest will help the tailbone to drop downward a little and your spine to straighten. Dropping the tailbone and sinking the chest forces your legs to carry more of the workload and this is exactly what we want. (Note that while we are looking for a relatively straight spine in the "Throwing the Ball" lessons, curvature is normal when going about every day life. I don't recommend you intentionally tuck your tailbone or use any of the previously mentioned constraints except for exploratory purposes.)

4. Repeat a few times and then rest in standing.

5. Decrease the distance in which you place your right foot from the midline (previously it was 12 inches) and repeat the steps, noticing how it changes the feel of the rotation in both directions as well as your sense of balance. Increase the distance beyond 12 inches and notice how it changes the feel. Play with different distances each time you come back to his lesson, each time searching for more balance while in full rotation.

6. Rest and notice how one leg is more rooted into the floor. One arm will probably feel much longer as well.

7. Take a walk and notice how much power you have in pushing off your right foot. The two sides of your body probably feel very different from each other.

8. Repeat as many steps as you want on the other side. When you are finished, go for a short walk or run to enjoy the increased power in your stride.

# Lesson 7

# Throwing the Ball 7: Lifting All Your Toes

## Stabilizing and Elongating Your Spine

**Starting Position:** Return to the familiar stance for throwing the imaginary baseball with your right hand (left foot forward). Leave your arms resting at your sides.

1. Lift all of the toes on your left foot high in the air. Notice how certain toes do not lift as easily. Notice that the higher your toes lift, the more your weight shifts back toward your heel. Go up and down a few times slowly with your toes feeling how this affects the top of your foot, your ankle and your shin.

2. Keeping your toes high in the air, begin to crush out the cigarette with the 1st metatarsal joint of your right foot. Go slowly so that you can be attentive to the following:

   a. When does your weight begin to shift off your 1st metatarsal joint and onto your 2nd, 3rd, 4th and/or 5th?

   b. When do the toes on your left foot begin to drop? Which toes drop first? For many people, the toes will begin to drop as soon almost as they begin rotating.

3. The next time you are fully rotated with your right knee pointing leftward toward your left knee, check the toes on your left foot and lift them as high as you can—especially the little toe—then slowly reverse the rotation on your right foot. Repeat as many times as you like, then rest. In resting, your two feet will feel quite different from each other.

4. Repeat the last step as you sink your chest back and downward almost as if to slouch—in order to keep your upper body directly over your pelvis. The sinking of your chest will help the tailbone to drop downward a little and your spine to straighten. Once again, dropping the tailbone and sinking the chest forces your legs to carry more of the workload and this is exactly what we want.

5. Walk around a little to compare the differences, then repeat each stop on the other side (with your right foot forward).

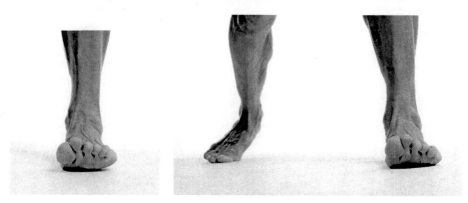

Lift all the toes of your front foot and keep them up

Remember to drop your chest and tailbone

# Lesson 8

# Throwing the Ball 8:  Eversion

## Stabilizing and Elongating Your Spine

**Starting Position:** Return to the familiar stance for throwing the imaginary baseball with your right hand (left foot forward). Leave your arms resting at your sides.

1.  As with Lesson 7, lift all the toes on your left foot high in the air and see to it that you are not leaning forward (drop your tailbone). Now begin to evert your left foot—that is, lift the outside edge of your left foot:  the little toe will begin to rise a little and the big toe will sink a little. Notice how the 1st metatarsal joint of your left foot begins to sink more into the ground. Also notice how your left knee moves a little inward (to the right)

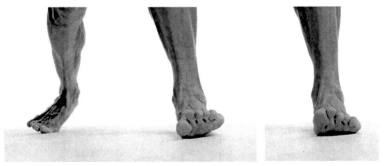

Notice the difference between everted (photo on left)
and not everted (right)

---

a.  With your left foot in this position, begin to slowly rotate on the 1st metatarsal joint of your right foot. This will probably feel like a balancing act in the beginning so go slowly. You don't need to make a large movement.
b.  As you rotate on the 1st metatarsal of your right foot, notice how the outside edge of your left foot wants to drop. See to it that your left foot stays

strongly everted—that is, the outside edge stays up in the air. The simple act of maintaining eversion in your left foot will cause something new to happen all the way up your left leg—from foot to ankle to knee to hip—and even through your ribcage.

   c.   Go back and forth a few times and initially keep the movements very small— I recommend you start by rotating just an inch to begin with. Over time as your system begins to understand and coordinate the movement better, you can increase the degree of rotation. Rest.

2.   Repeat step 1 and notice how maintaining eversion in your left foot while lifting all your toes sends your left hip backward and actually increases the stability in your left knee. Lead the movement with your left hip moving backward (allow your right foot to follow and see to it that you stay on the 1st metatarsal joint). Do this a few times and rest.

3.   Lead the movement from your right foot again and see if it feels easier. Then alternate between leading with your right foot and leading with your left hip. Do this a few times and rest.

4.   Finally, repeat the last step while sinking your chest back and downward almost as if to slouch—in order to keep your upper body directly over your pelvis. Once again, the sinking of your chest will help the tailbone to drop downward a little and your spine to straighten. Your legs will have to work more while your lower back will probably feel relieved.

Once again, remember to drop your chest and tailbone

5.   In standing, notice how different your two legs feel. Your shoulders and arms will probably feel quite different as well. In fact, there is likely a change through the entire half of your body making even the two sides of your face feel different (which side of your face feels more relaxed or longer?). Take a walk and compare your two sides.

6.   Repeat each step on the other side.

# Lesson 9

# Where Does My Arm Begin?
# ("Reach & Roll on Your Side")

## Primary Axis of Rotation: X-Axis

**Starting Position:** Lie on your right side and draw your knees up toward your chest such that your thighs make a 90 degree angle with your torso. Have your right arm straight out in front of you and rest your left hand comfortably on top of the right. Notice the texture of your right hand.

1.  Begin to very slowly slide your left hand forward a little, exploring the feeling of your right hand beneath it. Then slide your hand back to where it started. Go back and forth very slowly, each time trying to make the movement easier and less effortful. Ask yourself, "Where does my arm begin?" As you continue the movement, you may find yourself reaching beyond your right hand. This is not so much a goal as a possibility. How could it happen?

    a.  Notice what is moving besides your hand. For example, what is your elbow doing? Your left shoulder? What about your head? Do the movement with your eyes closed and notice if your head begins to turn. Could the movement of your head have any connection with the movement of your hand?

Optional: place firm support under your head
if your neck feels uncomfortable

---

Bird's eye view of steps 1.a - 1.b

b.  After exploring the movement several times rest on your back.

2.  Roll over to the same side and come to the same position. Now begin to slide your left hand back so that you can feel the contour of your right wrist, forearm and eventually the crook of your right elbow. While you do this, keep your left elbow relatively straight. Note that keeping the left elbow straight does not require that you lock the elbow (in fact locking it will probably be less comfortable). It may seem difficult or even impossible to slide the hand very far while the elbow stays fairly straight. Could moving some other part of your body would make the movement possible? For the next minute or two continue searching for ways to slide your hand backward without bending the elbow. If you are still wondering how to do it, continue wondering, knowing that wondering is far more important than "getting it right" (maybe there is no "right"). Give yourself permission to forget about the lesson do something else altogether.

If you choose to continue with the lesson, rest on your back for a few moments before continuing.

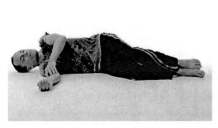

3.  Roll over to the same side and come to the same position and once again wonder where your left arm begins. Let go of the first answer that comes to mind. Then let go of the second. And the third. Slide your left hand forward and then bring it back to where it was initially resting. Go back and forth several times before pausing.

    a.  Imagine there is a button directly in front of your left knee and that you want to push it. Reach forward gently with your left knee to push the button. Note that forward, in this case, does not mean toward your chest. In addition, keep in mind that you don't need to lift your leg—in other words, it can stay in contact with the other leg—and you don't need to lift your ankle.

b. Go slowly so that you can really feel what is happening. Each time you slide the knee forward, and then back to neutral, notice what's happening in your left hip. Is there movement in your back? Is your left shoulder moving at all? What could be preventing your knee from moving further (without exerting more effort)? Again, note that it doesn't matter whether or not your knee moves further or whether you "get it right." Possibly what matters the most is knowing that it doesn't matter. Rest on your back.

4. Roll over to the same position. Slide both your left knee and left hand forward at the same time. If there were a mirror in front of you, your hand would be reaching toward the hand in the mirror and your knee toward the knee in the mirror. Try to move hand and knee in total synchrony so that one does not go faster than the other. Go slowly enough so that you notice when one or the other begins to get ahead.

a. Go forward and then back to neutral several times slowly, noticing when the movement is not so smooth. Cut your speed down to one fifth of the original. This means really slow down. (One trick I use for myself is to measure time: if it originally took me one second to complete the movement, then one fifth the speed would mean completing the movement in five seconds)

b. Try leading the movement once with your knee, and then once with your hand—alternate back and forth several times. Notice how leading with a different part changes the movement. Pause.

c. Slide your left hand forward and back to neutral. Notice if the movement has gotten easier and that you able to reach farther without any strain. Even if the movement doesn't feel easier, trust that over time—perhaps not today—it will. From a neurological perspective, things have already begun to change as a result of your slow exploration. From a Bagua perspective, you have already begun unblocking *qi*.

d. Lie on your back. Notice how one leg feels much longer than the other. You may feel that one arm also feels longer. It may feel like the floor is tilting to the right of left. This means that excessive muscle tension has just disappeared from half of your body, allowing that half to rest more fully into the floor. If you really pay attention, you will notice that half of you is expanding more as you inhale. This is because you have actually increased the breathing capacity in half of your body.

5. Roll over to the same side. Slide your left knee backward—as if the button now pushes back into your knee. Slide back and return to neutral several times. Notice if your back and shoulder are moving along with your knee. You may find your left hand sliding backward automatically. Go back and forth a few times before pausing.

a. As you slide your knee backward, intentionally slide your left hand backward while keeping your elbow relatively straight. See if you can slide the two in complete synchrony. Be lazy so that you minimize effort. For example, see if you can slide your arm without tensing your shoulder. Go back and forth a few times before pausing.

b.  Now simply slide your hand backward (still keeping your elbow relatively straight). Can you feel your back and ribcage turning with you? Go back and forth a few times slowly before pausing.

c.  Now slide your knee backward. What parts of your body are moving besides your knee? Go back and forth several times with your knee, sensing what else is moving.

d.  Now slide both knee and hand all the way forward and all the way backward. Note that at some point in going backward, your knee will begin to lift automatically without effort. Allow it to do so. Close your eyes. As you slide forward, allow your head to turn so that your nose comes toward the floor. As you slide backward, allow your head to turn so that your nose begins to point toward the ceiling. Go back and forth several times slowly, paying attention so that your neck stays soft and comfortable and that your head turns only as far as is extremely comfortable.

Allow your head to follow (rather than lead) the movement
of the rest of your body

e.  Pause and simply slide your hand forward and backward, keeping your eyes closed. Has the movement gotten easier? Once again, ask yourself, "I wonder where my arm begins." Rest on your back and notice how different the right and left sides of your body feel. One side is resting much more into the floor because parasitic tension has left that side. You have increased the flow of qi on that side.

6.  Repeat steps 1-5 lying on your other side.

7.  When you are finished, both sides will feel more even and you may find that your whole body is sinking more into the floor. Now a great deal of parasitic tension has left both sides of the body. The qi now flows more easily through your entire body.

8.  Take your time to slowly roll over and stand up. Close your eyes and feel how open your chest has become and how much lower your shoulders are resting. Do

you feel taller? Are you more grounded in your feet? Does your chest feel like it's floating? All of these remarkable changes have occurred through slowing down, wondering and observing. You have dissolved parasitic tension while simultaneously awakening dormant parts of yourself. In the process, qi has been unblocked and is flowing more freely through your body. Take a few moments to savor this feeling. Then open your eyes and take a walk, noticing how different walking feels.

# Lesson 10

# Standing Tall Without Trying to Stand Tall

## Stabilizing and Elongating Your Spine

**Experiment:** Walk up a flight of stairs and feel how much effort it requires and which muscles are getting tired. Do it a few times testing what happens when you look down at your feet compared to looking straight forward. Compare leaning forward more to leaning forward less. After getting a sense of how different ways of climbing stairs affect your sense of effort, try the following lesson.

**Starting Position:** Lie on your stomach, turn your head to the right and place your hands palm down, under your cheek with the right hand on top. Lift your head once. From a scale of 1 to 10, how heavy is it?

1. Imagine your left cheek is glued to the back of your right hand. Lift your head and right arm at the same time. See to it that your elbow and hand stay at the same height. Go up and down, feeling the parts of your back that start to get activated. Notice if you feel your buttocks contracting. Continue two or three times very slowly—go slowly enough that it takes five seconds to reach the top and five to reach the bottom. Rest with your head turned to the left.

2. Turn your head back to the right and keeping your left leg straight, begin to lift

your left foot in the air. Feel the muscles in your buttocks and back that begin to get activated as your foot goes higher. Move your foot straight toward the ceiling and then try different angles—for example, toward the ceiling and to the right a few degrees. Feel how lifting your foot in different angles affects the movement of your pelvis and back differently. Each variation literally activates different muscles all the way up your spine. Rest with your head turned to the left.

3.  Return to having your head turned to the right. Lift your head, right arm and left foot all at the same time. Does your head feel lighter? When any part of your body feels heavy, it is often because other parts are not activated. In this case, activating parts of your lower back and even your buttock help to lift your head. Notice if you are tightening your abs, which makes the movement more difficult. Try inflating your abdominal region, pushing it into the floor. Does this make the movement easier? Repeat a few times and rest.

4.  Return to the previous position. This time lift your right foot while lifting your head and right arm. How is this in comparison to doing it with your left foot? Repeat a few times.

5.  Repeat each step in the opposite configuration (with your head turned to the left and your left hand on top of the right).

6. Finally, place your forehead on your hands (either hand on top) and lift your head and both arms together. Explore a few times noticing the activation of muscles all the way down to your buttocks. Even your feet will move a little.

   a. Now try the movement while lifting both feet at the same time: which lifts higher, your head or your feet?

   b. As a variation, try it a few times with your chin resting on your right hand. Lift your right arm, head and right foot at the same time. Repeat a few times and then try lifting your right arm, head and left foot at the same time. Repeat a few times and then rest before trying it with your left arm.

   c. With your chin on your hands, lift your head, arms and both legs. Repeat a few times, sensing which elbow and which foot lift higher. Rest.

   d. Go back to having your head turned to the right. Lift it slowly once or twice to see if it's gotten lighter. From a scale of 1 to 10, how heavy is it now?

7. When you stand, notice how tall and erect you are. Climb a flight of stairs or walk up a hill with this tallness. Notice how much easier it is to climb when you are standing tall, rather than leaning forward. I've found that the difference is quite dramatic. I play with hills regularly and it never ceases to amaze me that certain ways of carrying my head and lifting upward give me so much more power. It's

like adding "turbo charge" to my stride.

## Lesson 11

# Lift Your Knees (On Your Back, Raising Knee Toward Chest and Ceiling)

**Starting Position:** Lie on your back with your left leg bent and left foot standing on the floor. Lift your right knee toward your chest so that your right leg hangs comfortably by itself somewhere above your right hip and abdomen.

1. Begin to lift your right knee up toward your chest (allow your leg to stay bent). How heavy does it feel? What are you doing with your left leg? Try this a few times to really test the heaviness of your right leg. Pause. Now push your right knee forward toward the ceiling. Does it move at all? Is it even possible? Pause.

   a. Lift your left foot an inch off the floor and continue testing the heaviness of your right knee going toward your chest. Does it feel heavier or lighter?

   b. Now press your left foot into the floor as you lift your knee. Push such that your left hip actually lifts an inch off the floor. Your left knee will move away from you. Notice how the action of your left leg changes the movement of your right knee. Feel how much easier it is to lift your left knee up toward your chest. It is now possible to push your knee toward the ceiling. Feel how much power you have. To up and down several times slowly.

   Many people lift their legs somewhat independently of the rest of their body when walking or running. Yet lifting one knee without pushing back with the opposite leg dramatically decreases their power. In a moment you will discover how involving the upper body further adds to your power.

2. Hold the front of your right knee with your left hand. Get a good grip (your thumb should be touching your index finger and all fingers should be pointing to the right). Begin to pull your knee up toward your left shoulder.
   What are you doing with your left leg? Rest.
   Notice how your left shoulder moves toward your right knee as well. Which way does your head want to roll? (Remember, if your eyes lock on a target, it will likely freeze your neck muscles and stop your head from moving freely) Play with this movement for a while searching for what your head really wants to do. Close your

eyes and see if it helps to free your neck.

3.  Go back to the same configuration (holding your right knee with your left hand) and continue pulling your knee toward your shoulder and allow your shoulder to move toward your knee. Begin pushing with your left foot into the floor and notice how much more your knee lifts—both toward your shoulder and toward the ceiling. Repeat several times and rest.

4.  Leave your arms at your sides and continue pushing with your left foot into the floor. This time reach your knee closer and closer to the ceiling. You will be pushing with quite a bit of force with your left leg. Which muscles are working in your left buttock? Feel how connected your right knee is to the extension of your left hip (photos below). Experiment with placing your left foot in different locations on the floor Go up and down a few times while your foot is in each new location, noticing which locations give you more power to raise your right knee. Rest.

5.  This time lift your head, shoulders and upper back off the floor before you begin (like doing a partial sit-up, your chest will come toward the ceiling). You can either hold your right knee with your left hand (as in the figure below) or simply leave both arms resting at your sides. Now begin to push your knee forward toward the ceiling. Go forward toward the ceiling and back down a few times. You will notice that two things happen:  1) your knee doesn't move as far as before, and 2) the movement is much more effortful. Lifting your shoulders and head has pushed your center of gravity down into your hips, making it much more difficult to extend your left hip. Your left leg now has much more weight to push against. Note that this configuration is a simulation of what happens when you lean too far forward when running.

6.  After you have rested, repeat each step on the other side.

# Lesson 12

# Mobilizing Your Ribcage

## Primary Axes of Rotation: X, Y and Z-Axes

**Starting Position:** Lie on your back and bend your knees so that your feet are flat on the floor. Hold the outside edge of your left foot with your left hand. Hold your left knee with your right hand. Slowly, begin to lift your foot in the air. Be gentle and go up and down noticing what happens in your left shoulder and in your neck.

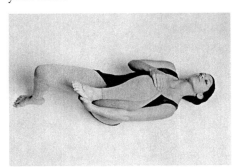 

1.  As your foot moves toward the ceiling you will feel muscles in your left leg becoming very active. Your hamstrings will begin to elongate. Move your leg up and down easily and smoothly. Rest after going up and down a few times.

2.  Return to the same configuration, but this time hold the back of your head with your right hand. Begin to lift your left foot and head at the same time, slowly. Try turning your head in different directions as you lift. Explore the simultaneous lifting of your head and foot several times, resting whenever you want. Notice how differently your leg moves in this configuration.

3.  Now try holding the inside of your left foot with your right hand and the back of your head with your left hand. Explore this movement several times, resting whenever you want. Notice how differently your leg and entire spine move compared to the previous configuration. Take a full rest with your arms and legs long. Notice how different the two sides of your body feel. Which leg and arm feel longer? Which side of your face feels longer?

4.  Go through steps 1-3 while holding the other foot and knee (hold the outside edge of your right foot with your right hand). Rest and compare your two sides.

5.  Reach between your legs and hold the inside arch of your right foot with your right hand (the palm of your hand should be against the arch of your foot), and the inside arch of your left foot with your left hand. Begin to raise your feet toward the ceiling. Try it a few times without lifting your head, but still allowing it the freedom to move (your chin may begin to move away from your chest while the back of your head slides toward the area between your shoulders). Then repeat several times while lifting your head at the same time. How is it different when you lift your head? Feel how each movement activates your thighs. What is happening in your shoulders and neck? Can you explore the movement without tensing up your shoulders or locking your elbows?

6.  Reach between your legs again, but this time hold the outside of each foot: the right palm is on top of the right foot and the fingers wrap around the outside

edge of the right foot; the left hand does the same on the left foot. Lift the feet several times toward the ceiling. Try it without lifting your head a few times before doing it while you lift your head. Compare the differences. Rest.

7.  Hold the front of your left knee with your left hand and the arch of your left foot with your right hand. Bring your knee toward your chest and your head toward your knee. Experiment with aiming your knee at different parts of your chest on both your left and right side.
    a.  Now switch your hands so that your right hand is on your left knee and your left hand reaches around the outside of your leg to the hold the outside of your left foot. Bring your knee toward your chest and head toward your knee at the same time.
    b.  Go back and forth, switching hands to compare the difference in how your left hip moves. Also notice how your ribcage and shoulders move (among other differences). Rest.

8.  Hold your left knee with your right hand and the outside of your left foot with your left hand. Begin to make circles with your left heel. Go slowly and see if you can make more and more accurate circles (rather than ovals). Make sure you lift your head off the floor so you can watch your foot. After a few repetitions, change directions. Make sure you rest whenever you need to. Optional: if you can do so without strain, repeat the motion, but this time allow your head to rest on the floor—notice how the ribcage and hip move differently.

**Mobilizing Your Ribcage**

9. Repeat steps 7 and 8 on the other side.
10. (Advanced Step) Reach between your legs and hold the insides of your arches with your hands. Begin to reach the sole of your left foot toward the ceiling as your right knee reaches toward the floor. Go slowly and see how well you can control the movement. Once your right knee touches (your left leg will be relatively straight), reverse the movement until your right leg is relatively straight and your left knee is touching the ground. Go back and forth slowly. Note that you do not have to touch the floor with either knee if it is a strain.

Try doing the movement while lifting your head and compare it to doing it while allowing your head to roll on the floor. Both variations are useful.

11. Optional: Repeat step 5 and see if it is easier. Repeat step 6 and see if it is easier. If you want, you can try any of steps 1-4 to see if they have become easier.
12. Stand up and notice how full your breath has become and how light your shoulders and chest feel. Do you feel more rooted into your legs? Walk and see if your upper body feels longer and lighter.

# Lesson 13

# Using Your Butt to Lift You Up

1. Find a sizeable hill to walk up. Use chalk or some other means to measure out 6 inch intervals.
2. As you begin to walk, lift your knees higher and higher—exaggerate your motion to bring your knees very high.
3. Notice how your arms and shoulders start to get more involved as your knees go higher. Are you looking down are your feet?
4. As we shall see in the next lesson, the way you use your Achilles tendons, calf muscles and indeed, your entire lower body is inextricably linked to what you do with your head. For now notice what's happening with the back of your neck: is it curving more or less than usual? Is it bending forward? If you are not doing so already, look straight ahead into the distance rather than down. Your gaze will influence the elongation of your spine.
5. Start to stride easily, but do not try to cover a lot of ground. Intentionally drive your knees upward as if you are trying to stride over a barrier. This way you will be traveling more upward than forward. Again, check the back of your neck to see if it is long and straight. Make sure you are looking into the distance and not downward.
6. See if you can cover no more than 6 inches per stride.
7. Do this for about one minute, then rest for a few minutes, then continue to the next step.
8. Run up the hill, and continue focusing on lifting your knees and keeping the back of the neck long. Do not attempt to cover as much ground as possible. See if you can continue to stay tall rather than leaning forward. How does staying tall affect your stride? See if you feel your legs working differently than usual. Do you feel more power?

# Lesson 14

# Water Jugs, Furniture and Other Things to Carry on Your Head

## Primary Axis of Rotation:  Z-Axis

## Stabilizing and Elongating Your Spine

**Starting Position:** Sit at the edge of a sturdy, armless chair (preferably with little or no cushioning so that you can really feel your sitz bones on the chair) with your feet firmly planted on the floor. Close your eyes and use one index finger to touch the bony protuberance at the top of your neck—where your neck meets your skull. This is your occiput. Place your other index finger on the middle of your chin.

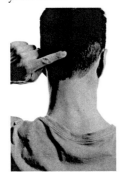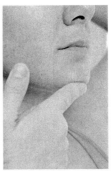

1.  Begin to collapse the back of your neck so that your chin juts further and further forward. Your chest will also begin to collapse and you will begin to hunch. Most of us are doing some less exaggerated version of this in daily life even though it may be causing us neck and back pain. Notice how the occiput begins to move down toward the ground as the chin moves forward and up. They move in opposite directions.

Notice how her entire spine moves with the movement of her head.

2. Now begin to do the opposite. Begin to lengthen the back of your neck such that your chin starts to come in toward your throat. You will feel your occiput start to rise. You will also feel some part of the top of your head reaching for the sky. Which part is it?

3. If you lengthen the back of the neck beyond a certain point, your head will start to tip so that your nose (and thus your face) ends up pointing downward. If you don't lengthen enough, your nose will be pointing a little upward. Go back and forth slowly and start to get a sense of the middle point where the back of your neck is long and you feel effortlessly tall. Sense how at this point, a certain part of your head reaches for the sky. You have just discovered a vital point on the top of your head. Bagua masters call this point the *Baihui* (pronounced, "bye-whey"), which translates to the convergence of all yang meridians.

In the first image, the *Baihui* is reaching for the sky.

4. Repeat the previous steps, with your hands switched (if your right index finger was on your chin, place it on your occiput). If you use a mirror, you will notice that your head will naturally turn toward whichever hand you place in front.

5. Imagine a hook connected to your *Baihui* being pulled gently toward the sky as if you were a marionette.

6. Stand up and try walking while you collapse the back of your neck so that your chin begins to jut forward. Notice that the more you collapse your neck, the more

your chest sinks in and the heavier your body feels. Now attempt to lengthen the back of your neck and notice how this feels in comparison. Lifting the top of your head actually helps to lift your ribcage. Thus, in lifting your *Baihui*, you will likely feel not only more comfortable, but more powerful. You are beginning to tap into a critical technique used by Bagua masters, good runners, and, indeed millions of women around the world who transport everything from water and food, to clothing and furniture on top of their heads.*

---

* Obviously you don't have to be a Taichi master to have an intuitive understanding of the *Baihui*. People throughout the world have been using their heads in efficient ways for eons.
As with maintaining balance, discovering your *Baihui*, requires constant searching. You are searching for the feeling of pushing up from the top of your head in a way that makes you feel tall, strong, at ease and confident all at the same time. The taller, stronger and more at ease you feel, the more you know that your *Baihui* is rising toward the sky.

# Lesson 15

# Reaching for the Sky

## Stabilizing and Elongating Your Spine

*This next lesson involves the supremely rejuvenating activity of skipping and provides a nice complement to Lesson 13 ("Using Your Butt to Lift You Up"). Skipping allows me to feel very light, as if I'm floating. In fact, for a split second, I am floating—and I imagine I'm Michael Jordan gliding through the air before dunking the ball. You can get enormous lift out of skipping—often more so than simply by jumping—and the activity brings levity not just to my body, but my mood (Maybe a lack of skipping is one reason we adults and teenagers tend to be too serious). Skipping is such a delightful activity that it's a shame more of us don't do it. I myself stopped skipping for decades because it simply wasn't a "cool" thing to do once I became a teenager.*

**Starting Position:** In standing, cross your arms at the wrists and interlace your fingers. Slowly bring your hands toward the sky. Your arms will come toward your ears and your elbows will begin to straighten.

1. Take your time to play with the gradual straightening of your elbows while bringing your arms backward as if you wanted to use them to squeeze the back of your head. Be gentle as the goal is not to "get there" but rather, to go in the direction of straightening (without locking) the elbows.

Notice how your entire chest begins to lift. Also notice how your lower back begins to arch. To counter this, drop your tailbone. You will feel your lower back flattening and the weight dropping more into your legs.

Can you see how the spine is curving and shortening rather than straightening and elongating in each of these examples?

Dropping your tailbone allows for an expansion of your lower back. Breathe down and back into this area and feel how it expands even more. Rest and walk around.

In these examples the spine is elongating in the directed manner.

2. Resume the previous position and this time, begin to walk. Lift your knees higher and higher, as if you were in the marching band. As you lift your knees, simultaneously straighten your elbows and reach for the sky with your hands. The resultant lifting of your ribcage will actually help to lift your knees higher. Continue marching like this for a while, then rest.

3. Resume the previous position and begin marching again. After marching a few steps, begin to skip, lifting your knees higher and higher toward the sky. Each time you lift a knee, reach higher with your hands. Again, the lifting of your hands and thus, ribcage helps to pull your knees up. Feel how much lift and power you get as a result. Continue for a while, and whenever you want, drop your arms but continue skipping.

    a. Allow your arms to pump upward: as your left leg lifts, your right arm will lift. Reach your elbow toward your midline (the line that divides the right and left halves of your body) and upward toward the sky at the same time. The direction in which your elbow and thus, shoulder and thorax travel re-

lates crucially to how much thrust you get in your legs. Play with reaching your elbow in different directions, searching for which angles give you more lift.

b.   Notice if your knees travel straight or toward the midline, then intentionally drive your knees toward the midline as you skip.

c.   Rest and walk around.

4.   Return to reaching for the sky with interlaced fingers (arms crossed). Begin walking and at some point, begin skipping, using your arms to help lift your body.

a.   Whenever you want, drop you arms but continue skipping, noting the trajectory of your elbows.

b.   At some point simply begin to run. See if you feel taller and more powerful. Does your stride feel more powerful? Rest whenever you want.

5.   As an option, repeat any of the steps, but with your hands interlaced in the non-habitual fashion (with the opposite thumb on top).

# Lesson 16

# Salsa Hips

## Primary Axis of Rotation: Y-Axis

*Modern footwear, chairs and even ideas on fitness and morality have con-tributed to narrowing ranges of motion in people throughout much of the "civi-lized" world.\* As mentioned earlier, footwear tends to act as a substitute for ten-dons, muscles and your nervous system, thereby limiting what your body would oth-erwise do. The elevated and padded heels that we see in virtually all running shoes, for example, keeps your heels from reaching all the way to the earth and thereby, prevents your spine from elongating (through rotation, sideflexion and extension) in order to facilitate that reach. The result is a weaker, less fluid and less comfortable gait in walking and stride in running.*

*Feldenkrais Trainer, Frank Wildman, has astutely observed that by dis-couraging the swaying of our hips when we walk, certain cultural forces (such as conservative sexual mores) have even further limited how we use our spine. Due to its greater width, a woman's pelvis will naturally sway more than a man's when she is walking unless, of course, she inhibits the motion by tightening her "core" and ribcage unnecessarily. Even efficient walking among men relies on some hip sway, albeit to a lesser degree. For either gender, chronic holding in your core, ribcage and spine—whether imposed by footwear, morals or ideas on fitness and aesthetics—decreases power and fluidity. Thus, whether I'm trying not to walk "suggestively" or simply following the current fashion of sucking in my gut and tightening my abs, I am inadvertently restraining my own power. The following lesson will help to reinstate a suppleness in your pelvis and spine that are important for powerful walking and running. You may notice that in the 10-20 minutes it takes to explore this lesson the length of your gait has actually increased in length.*

---

\* Galen Cranz has written a marvelous book called, *The Chair: Rethinking Culture, Body and Design*, detailing how chairs have negatively impacted human posture.

**Starting Position:** Stand with your feet about hip-width apart. Reach over the top of your head with your right hand such that the palm is somewhere on the crown and the fingers extend toward your left ear.

1. Begin to bring your right elbow down toward your right hip. Notice what is the first thing that moves. Repeat a few times, each time with the intention of locating what moves first: this is likely the place from which you are initiating. Also notice how the weight shifts on your feet. Does it shift more to the right foot or to the left foot? It is important that you not stretch your neck during this lesson. In fact, I recommend minimizing the movement of your neck. How can you move your right elbow toward your right hip yet keep your neck from stretching at the same time?

Make sure the bending is distributed evenly throughout your entire spine.

Over-stretching the neck: a common error when the spine doesn't bend.

2. Return to the starting position and this time intentionally shift your weight to your left foot as your bring your right elbow toward your hip. Can you feel how much easier the movement becomes? Do this a few times and then compare it to shifting your weight onto your right foot while your elbow drops. Notice how shifting more to the right foot locks your pelvis and ribcage in place. To move further you have to stretch your upper body and/or your neck. Powerful move-

ment generally relies on a more "democratic" distribution of work such that no one part gets stretched more than another. Continue once or twice and see to it that you are not stretching your neck in the process—your neck should not feel any strain from these movements—if it does, then stop immediately. Rest and notice how much longer you feel on one side compared to the other. Does your right arm feel longer? Is your right shoulder lower?

3.  Return to the starting position and continue to explore the movement. This time notice that as you shift your weight to the left, your right heel gets lighter and lighter. Your right knee is bending. Allow your right hip to be totally free and this will allow your leg to just "hang" from the joint. If you really allow it this freedom, you'll feel your right knee starting to point to the right even as it swings to the left. Go back and forth a few times, giving your right leg more and more freedom. Rest. The two sides of your body will feel more and more different.

4.  Place your right hand on the right side of your ribcage with your thumb in back and the other four fingers in front. My students call this the "teapot" position (your right arm being the handle). Begin to lower your right elbow toward your right hip. Again, allow your weight to shift to your left foot. Feel how, like an accordion, the ribs on your right side squeeze together as your elbow goes down and come apart as your elbow comes up. This movement in the ribcage (called, "sidebending") contains elements that are important to walking and running. Indeed, many movements in your ribcage are crucial to giving you power. Repeat a few times, then go back to the starting position with your hand on your head. Bring your elbow downward and see how much easier it is than when you started the lesson. Feel how your body is moving together in unison. Rest.

5.  Walk around and notice how much looser your right hip feels. Does your right foot reach farther forward with each step? Can you feel how your left shoulder is leading more than usual as you walk? Feel how you push off with more power in your left foot.

6.  Repeat each step on the other side.

Avoid bending in any direction except strictly sideways. The examples above illustrate bends outside of the desired plane.

# Lesson 17

# Reach & Roll on Your Back

## Primary Axis of Rotation:  X-Axis

**Starting Position:** Lie on your back and bend your right leg so that your right foot stands firmly on the floor.

1.  Reach for the ceiling with your right hand. Notice if you have a habit of locking your elbow when you reach for things. What would prevent your arm for going higher without dislocating your shoulder? Ask yourself, "Where does my arm begin?" Rest.

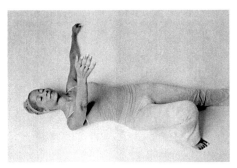

2.  Gently push into the floor with your right foot. What happens to your right hip? What about your left hip? Push slowly and release just as slowly. Go back and forth, each time pushing a little further. Rest.

3.  This time push with your right foot, but with the clear intention of rolling your pelvis a little to the left and then returning to neutral. Try it a few times and notice if the movement feels easier and completely different as a simple result of changing your intention. Could it be that following the instruction, "push into the floor" led you to unconsciously lift your entire pelvis—the heaviest part of your body—off the floor? Doing so would indeed require a lot of effort. Yet, the greatest shifts in power occur through finding the easiest way to perform an action.

    a.  Continue looking for an easier, less effortful way to move. Is your left knee locked? See if you can let go of your left leg (unlock the knee if it is locked), thereby allowing your leg to roll to the left.

b. When you allow your pelvis to roll, your back turns to the left, beginning at the base of the lower back and traveling upward in a spiral—possibly all the way up to your neck. Continue slowly rolling your pelvis to the left and returning to neutral, each time sensing how your spine moves. Rest.

4. Return to the same configuration and this time experiment with placing your right foot in different locations. Each time you push from a new location, feel how different the movement is in your knee, hip and back. A simple shift of one inch in any direction will dramatically alter the way you use your muscles and joints and therefore how much power you get. Try at least 5 different locations, pausing to rest whenever you want to.

5. Knowing you are going to roll your pelvis to the left, place your right foot where you feel you will have the most power. This time as you push with your foot, reach for the ceiling with your right hand. Though your body will roll to the left, your hand can continue reaching toward the ceiling. What are you doing with your head?

a. Close your eyes to help free up the muscles in your neck.

b. Reach over your right shoulder with your left hand so that you can hold your shoulder. As you reach for the ceiling with your right hand, use your left hand pull on your right shoulder blade thereby helping to roll your body to the left. Your left elbow will travel to the left as you roll to your left. Continue pushing with your right foot.

 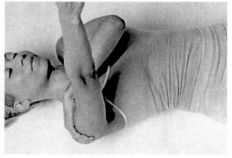

c. See if you can move more in synchrony—the right hand, left elbow and right hip moving all at the same time.

d. Notice how your right arm reaches higher than when you began, yet there is no added stress to your shoulder. Ask yourself, "Where does my arm begin?" Repeat a few times then place your arms on the floor.

e. Push once or twice slowly with your right foot and notice how much easier the movement has gotten and how much looser your back and neck have become. Rest.

6. As an option, you can repeat the previous step but this time reach under your armpit with your with your left hand. See that you can get a decent hold of the

bottom of your right shoulder blade with your left hand. Pulling this way with your left hand will act to mobilize your spine in a slightly different fashion than

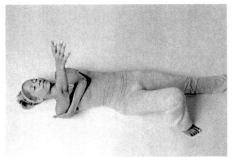 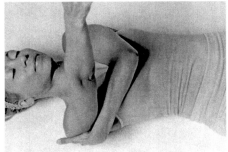

reaching over your shoulder. Repeat a few times and rest.

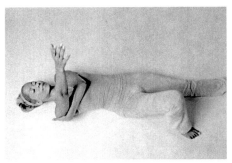 

Notice how her head follows the direction of her rolling. Another possibility is to allow your head to trail behind.

7.   Get up and walk around noticing the significant change on one side of your body. When you are ready, lie down and go through each step on the other side.

# Lessons 18 & 19

# "Boxer's Shuffle" Series

As with the some of the "Throwing the Ball" lessons, I recommend watching yourself in the mirror while doing the "Boxer's Shuffle" so that you can check your positioning (you will need a fairly large mirror to watch yourself shuffling). The mirror can help you become aware of when you are leaning or otherwise not maintaining the suggested constraints of the lesson. Videotaping your movements can be even more effective in revealing what it is you are really doing—rarely will it match up with what you thought you were doing.

# Lesson 18

# Boxer's Shuffle 1: Forward and Back

## Stabilizing and Elongating Your Spine

**Starting Position:** Return to the position of throwing an imaginary ball with your right hand. Stay on the 1st metatarsal joint of your right foot. This time, lift the entire ball of your left foot off the ground and pull all of your toes back (wear a shoe on this foot if it's too hard on your heel). Ideally, all that will be in touch with the floor are your left heel and the right big toe and 1st metatarsal joint of your right foot.

1. Take a small step forward with your left foot and then follow with your right. Continue for five steps. Then take a small step backward with your right foot and follow with your left. Continue for five steps.

   Go forward 5 steps and backward 5 steps, taking only small steps. Try going only one inch at a time. Rest after a few rounds of back and forth.

   If you carefully watch professional boxers, dancers, soccer players or point guards in the NBA, you'll notice that they all make very precise movements with their feet. Their footwork is what lends to their incredible balance, power and agility.

2. Resume the previous movement and this time notice the transition from going forward to backward. Does the ball of your foot start coming down during the transition? Do you begin leaning forward? See to it that you lean as little as possible and that your toes stay pulled back with the ball of your foot high off the floor. Slow down even more if it helps you to keep from leaning and prevents the ball of your foot from dropping. Attention to detail during this transition is important in teaching you how to keep your upper body directly over your pelvis. It is also important in teaching you how to generate more power with your feet and legs. Begin to notice the transition from backward to forward. Do you lean backward? Again, minimize any leaning. Slow down if it allows you to more accurately maintain the constraints. Rest after a few iterations.

3. This time, allow the ball of your foot to return to the floor, but evert your left

foot—that is, lift the outside edge of the foot. Repeat the forward and back and feel how different parts of your feet and legs are being awakened. Be vigilant: when does the outside edge of your left foot start to drop? What about your right foot? When you are ready, rest. Walk and notice the difference.

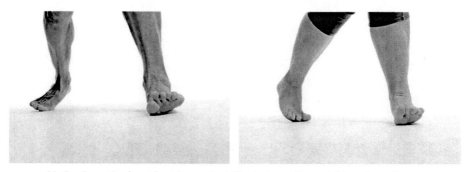

Notice how the front foot is everted. Try to keep the outside edge of your front foot as high as possible. Notice when it begins to drop.

4. Now allow yourself to shuffle forward and backward a few times with your whole left foot on the floor. Notice if you feel more power in moving back and forth. Rest.

5. When you are ready, repeat all the previous steps with your right leg forward. Over time, you will get stronger and be able to maintain the constraints of the lesson more precisely. Your footwork will improve and you will be able to go faster. Note that for the purposes of this lesson it is far better to take small, precise steps of just a few inches. Even one inch steps can be very good for learning. When the stepping gets too large, you start to lose precision and the movement starts to get clumsy. Again, precision and control are the key issue.

6. As a powerful variation to the "Boxer's Shuffle" lessons, combine them with Lesson 15 ("Reaching for the Sky") in order to drive home the importance of a long and stable spine while running. To combine the lessons, simply do the following before executing steps 1-5:

   a. In standing, cross your arms at the wrists and interlace your fingers. Slowly bring your hands toward the sky. Your arms will come toward your ears and your elbows will begin to straighten. Take your time to play with the gradual straightening of your elbows while bringing your arms backward as if you wanted to use them to squeeze the back of your head. Be gentle as the goal is not to "get there" but rather, to go in the direction of straightening the elbows.

   b. Notice how your entire chest begins to lift. Also notice how your lower back begins to arch. To counter this, drop your tailbone. You will feel your lower back flattening and the weight dropping more into your legs.

   c. Dropping your tailbone allows for an expansion of your lower back. Breathe down and back into this area and feel how it expands even more.

d.   Keeping your arms up, proceed with the steps 1-5.

7.   When you have finished exploring, walk and see how powerful and fluid your gait has become.  Try running for 50 meters and see what that feels like.

# Lesson 19

# Boxer's Shuffle 2:  Side to Side

## Stabilizing and Elongating Your Spine

**Starting Position:**  Return to the same starting position from Lesson 18 ("Boxer's Shuffle 1"):  use the same constraints with both feet, but this time move side to side rather than forward and back. When shuffling to the right, make sure that you step first with your right foot. Likewise, when shuffling to the left, make sure that you step first with your left foot. During the lesson, make sure you take small, precise steps. Finally, keep in mind that you can combine this lesson with Lesson 15 ("Reaching for the Sky") as well.

# Lesson 20

# Making Your Head Lighter

## Primary Axis of Rotation: Z-Axis

**Starting Position:** Lie on your back and feel how your shoulders are resting on the floor. Notice how wide they feel. Do they make much contact with the floor? Also notice how high the arch in your lower back is. Is it higher or lower than the arch in the back of your neck? Is your neck uncomfortable? If so, fold some towels neatly and place them under your head until your neck no longer feels strained. Slowly lift your head an inch off the floor to feel how heavy it is, then let it rest back on the floor. Take a measure from 1 to 10. 10 means your head is very heavy like a boulder. 1 means it's very light and easy to lift.

1. Bend your knees so that your feet are flat on the floor and about hip-width apart. Start to press gently with your feet. Do you feel your pelvis moving? What about your lower back? Press gently and let go gently. Go back and forth slowly, noticing if your pelvis is tilting and if your lower back is coming toward the floor. When the muscles in the lower back are chronically tense, they will hold the spine like an iron board and prevent it from curving easily into the ground. Lengthen your legs and rest.

2. Imagine that your spine is a keyboard. With the fingers of either hand, press into three "keys" in your lower spine (if for some reason you cannot reach your lower back with your hand, have somebody else do it for you). Once you have a clear sense of those three keys, remove your hand.

   a. Push with your feet and one by one, begin to bring each of the three keys you just located toward the floor. If your lower back is tense, you may need to engage your abdominal muscles in order to do this. Note that it isn't imperative that the three keys actually touch the floor. They only need to go toward the floor.

   b. Once you have done this, slowly reverse the movement so that the keys move away from the floor one by one. Go back and forth slowly, clearly feeling each point either touching or coming toward the floor. See if you can do the movement more and more smoothly. Notice if you are veering off to the right or left. Go slowly enough so that you can notice how precisely you are traveling up the middle of your spine.

c. Continue decreasing your speed until it takes five seconds to get all three points on the floor, and five seconds to reverse the movement. You may want to count slowly to yourself, "One…two…three…" in order to make sure you are really slowing down.

d. Rest with your legs long.

3. Bend your knees again and this time, begin to raise your lower back from the floor, making the arch higher. You can do this by rolling your pelvis forward and letting go of or even pushing out your lower abdomen. Rather than sucking in your gut you will be letting it hang out as the arch in your back rises. Go back and forth a few times before resting.

4. Feel the back of your head resting on the floor. Imagine you have some paint on that part of your head and you want to wipe it off onto the floor by sliding your head up and down, as if to nod.

a. Your chin will move toward your chest and away from your chest as you do this. Remember that you are sliding your head, not lifting it—your head should stay in contact with the floor in order to wipe the paint off. See to it that you make the movement smooth and easy. This is not intended to be a workout for your neck and it is not intended to stretch the neck so be very gentle. The movements do not have to be large.

b. What is it that prevents your head from moving further and more easily? Can you feel any movement in the center of your chest? What could your chest be doing in order to make the movement easier? Go back and forth several times.

c. Rest.

The photos above show the desired *direction* of head movement. Note that your head does *not* need to move as much as indicated. In fact, I recommend you keep the movement smaller than shown above.

5. Touch the bottom of your breastbone. To either side of this point you will discover a set of ribs branching off. Place the heels of your hands these ribs—the left hand will press on the left branch, the right hand on the right branch. Have your

fingers pointing in the direction of your pelvis.

a.   Raise your elbows a little and start to press with the heels of your hands as if you wanted to tuck your ribs downward into your pelvis. (Another way to think of this is to imagine that your upper body forms a big ball of dough with an air pocket beneath it. The air pocket is the arch in your lower back. By pressing with the heels of your hands you are flattening the dough and squeezing out the air pocket. The motion is similar to the motion of kneading bread.)

b.   Allow your lower back to come toward the floor as you press—this is what will allow the ribs to move. See to it that you press with the heels of your hands and not with your fingers. This will give you more power. Go back and forth several times slowly, trying to feel how the lower back can sink toward the floor. Can you feel your chest moving? Pause.

c.   Begin to slide your head on the floor as you push your ribs down toward your pelvis. Your chin moves away from your chest as you press (the back of your head slides toward the area between your shoulder blades), and moves back toward your chest as you stop pressing.

d.   Rest with your arms and legs long.

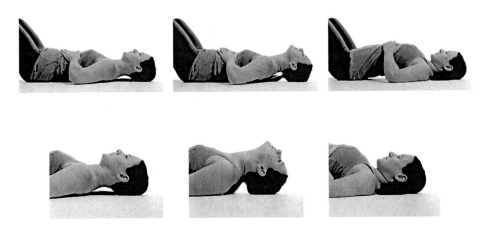

6.   Bend your legs and stand your feet on the ground about hip-width apart. Press gently into the floor with both feet. Notice if your lower back sinks more easily to the floor now. Can you feel those three points more distinctly touching the floor as you press? Go back and forth a few times very slowly and notice if your chest moves as you push. Notice if your head moves as well. If you sense more movement in your chest and head it means that chronically tense muscles between your hips and your chest and head have let go. Excessive muscle tension, in other words, is no longer blocking the force from traveling all the way up your spine.

a.   Place your hands on your ribs and simply slide your head on the floor as you did earlier. Go slowly. Can you feel your ribs moving and lower back sinking?

Even without pressing with your hands, your ribs may move automatically. Rest with arms and legs long.

b.  Notice if the arch in your lower back has gotten lower. Does the back of your neck feel longer? Are your shoulders resting more comfortably into the floor?

7.  Take your time to roll over and sit up and eventually stand up. Once in standing, close your eyes and notice how low and relaxed your shoulders are. They may feel like they are just hanging off your body, no longer rising with tension. Do you feel taller? Does your chest feel more open, as if it is floating? Do you feel more rooted in your feet? Walk around slowly and feel how comfortable walking is. The exploration on the floor has changed your muscle tone and woken up connections that have long been dormant.

# Attributions for Quotations

Page viii    Terry Gilliam, introduction to a screening of the film, *Tideland.*

Page xi    Margaret Mead, *Male and Female: A Study of the Sexes in a Changing World*, 19.

Page 1    Andre Agassi, *Open: An Autobiography*, 1.

Page 2    Trevor Leggett, *The Dragon Mask*, www.bestjudo.com (go to http://www.bestjudo.com/review/1989/dragon-mask and scroll down to the story called, "Training").

Page 5    Alan Watts, *The Culture of Counter Culture: The Edited Transcripts*, 58.

Page 6    Ari Weinzweig, *Zingerman's Guide to Good Eating*, 400.

Page 7    Alon, Ruthy, *Mindful Spontaneity: Lessons in the Feldenkrais Method*, 229.

Page 8    Josh Waitzkin, *The Art of Learning: A Journey in the Pursuit of Excellence*, 186-187.

Page 11    Eckhart Tolle, public lecture at UCLA Royce Hall, October 29, 2007.

Page 15    Agness De Mille, *Martha: The Life and Work of Martha Graham*, as quoted in Rosamund Stone Zander & Benjamin Zander, The Art of Possibility: Transforming Professional and Personal Life, 116.

Page 17    Albert Einstein, *Einstein Revealed*, broadcast on *Nova* in 1999. According to the producer, Thomas Levenson, this statement is a paraphrase of a few actual quotes combined together. "That quote was a collage of a couple of different Einstein aphorisms, I believe sourced from Alice Calaprice's The Quotable Einstein. In that documentary we operated under two rules: if the actor playing Einstein was speaking on camera, we would rewrite Einstein's original words as needed to transform written expression into speakable lines. If quoted in voice over, without seeing the actor's lips move, those quotes were exact (translations)." –Thomas Levenson (personal correspondence)

Page 17    Keith Johnstone, *Improvisation and the Theatre*, 80.

Page 19    Frank Wildman, *Change Your Age: Using Your Body and Brain to Feel Younger, Stronger, and More Fit*, 2.

Page 25    Stanley Keleman, *Your Body Speaks Its Mind*, 37-38.

Page 27    Alan Watts, "A Cure for Education", from *Talking Zen*, excerpted in *Mountains are Mountains and Rivers are Rivers*, edited by Ilana Rabinowitz, 27-28.

Page 29    Don Hanlon Johnson, *Body: Recovering Our Sensual Wisdom*, 81.

Page 35    Andre Agassi, *Open: An Autobiography*, 1.

Page 37    Neale Donald Walsch, *Conversations With God*, 170.

Page 38    Moshe Feldenkrais (one of the many sayings attributed to him by his students).

Page 40    W. Timothy Gallwey, *The Inner Game of Tennis*, 148.

Page 41    Charles Eisenstein, *Yoga of Eating*, public lecture in Philadelphia, PA, 2007.

Page 47    Dave Barry, *Miami Herald*, Dec. 1, 1996.

Page 56    Sly & the Family Stone, "Life," *Life*, Epic/CBS, 1968.

Page 59    Thomas Hanna, *Body of Life: Creating New Pathways for Sensory Awareness and Fluid Movement*, 38.

Page 61    James Gleick, *Genius: The Life and Science of Richard Feynman*, 227-228.

Page 65    Malcolm Gladwell, *Blink: The Power of Thinking Without Thinking*, 120-121.

Page 73    Thomas Hauser, *Muhammad Ali: His Life and Times*, 19.

Page 73    Dave Lowry, *Traditions: Essays on the Japanese Martial Arts and Ways*, 144.

Page 75    Ellen Langer, *On Becoming an Artist*, 151.

Page 87    Otto Pohl, "Improving the Way Humans Walk," *New York Times*, March 12, 2002.

Page 91    P.F. Flyers® by B.F. Goodrich®. 1960s TV Commercial. Seen on Youtube 10 September, 2010: <http://www.youtube.com/watch?v=1rUFlXZzbE8&feature=related>

Page 91    Shape-Ups® from Sketchers®. TV Advertisement. Seen on Youtube 10 September, 2010: <http://www.youtube.com/watch?v=71cvCXp8_Tk>

Page 99    Jess O'Brien, editor, *Nei Jia Quan: Internal Martial Arts*, 165.

Page 100     Thomas Merton, in a letter to Jim Forest dated February 21, 1966 reproduced in *Hidden Ground of Love: The Letters of Thomas Merton on Religious Experience and Social Concerns*, edited by William H. Shannon, 1993

Page 101     Charles Eisenstein, *The Ascent of Humanity*, 123.

Page 105     Don Hanlon Johnson, *Body: Recovering Our Sensual Wisdom*, 67-68.

Page 109     Deane Juhan, *Job's Body*, 253.

Page 113     Carl Sagan, *The Varieties of Scientific Experience*.

Page 116     Fritjof Capra, *Hidden Connections*, 126.

Page 119     Erich Schiffmann, *Yoga: The Spirit and Practice of Moving Into Stillness*, 3-4.

Page 122     Stanley Keleman, *Your Body Speaks Its Mind*, 63.

Page 123     Thomas Hanna, *Body of Life: Creating New Pathways for Sensory Awareness and Fluid Movement*, 34.

Page 124     Joseph Campbell, *Reflections on the Art of Living: A Joseph Campbell Companion*, edited by Diane K. Osbon, 26.

Page 126     Wolfe Lowenthal, *There Are No Secrets: Professor Cheng Man-ch'ing and his Tai Chi Chuan*, 40.

Page 129     Robert W. Smith, *Martial Musings: A Portrayal of the Martial Arts in the 20th Century*, 205.

Page 133     W. Timothy Gallwey, *Inner Tennis: Playing the Game*, 169.

# Bibliography

Agassi, Andre, *Open: An Autobiography*, New York: A. Knopf, 2009.

Alon, Ruthy, *Mindful Spontaneity: Lessons in the Feldenkrais Method*, Berkeley, CA: North Atlantic Books, 1996.

Barry, Dave, *Miami Herald*, Dec. 1, 1996.

Campbell, Joseph; edited by Diane K. Osbon, *Reflections on the Art of Living: A Joseph Campbell Companion*, New York: Harper Perennial, 1998.

Capra, Fritjof, *Hidden Connections*, New York: Anchor Books, 2004.

Cranz, Galen, *The Chair: Rethinking Culture, Body & Design*, New York: W.W. Norton, 1998.

De Mille, Agnes, *Martha: The Life and Work of Martha Graham*, New York: Random House, 1991.

Dreyer, Danny and Katherine, *Chi Running: A Revolutionary Approach to Effortless, Injury-Free Running*, New York: Fireside, 2009.

Eisenstein, Charles, *The Ascent of Humanity*, Harrisburg, PA: Panenthea, 2007.

Eisenstein, Charles, *Yoga of Eating*, public lecture in Philadelphia, PA, 2007.

Gallwey, W. Timothy, *The Inner Game of Tennis*, New York: Random House, Inc., 1974.

Gallwey, W. Timothy, *Inner Tennis: Playing the Game*, New York: Random House, Inc., 1976.

Gilliam, Terry seen on Youtube introducing his film, *Tideland*, 2006 (directed by Terry Gilliam).

Gladwell, Malcolm, *Blink: The Power of Thinking Without Thinking*, New York: Little, Brown Company, 2005.

Gleick, James, *Genius: The Life and Science of Richard Feynman*, New York: Pantheon Books, 1992.

Hanna, Thomas, *Body of Life: Creating New Pathways for Sensory Awareness and Fluid Movement*, Rochester, VT: Healing Arts Press, 1979.

Hauser, Thomas, *Muhammad Ali: His Life and Times*, New York: Simon & Schuster, 1991.

Johnson, Don Hanlon, *Body: Recovering Our Sensual Wisdom*, Berkeley, CA: North Atlantic Books, 1992.

Johnstone, Keith, *Improvisation and the Theatre*, New York: Routledge/Theatre Arts Books, 1992.

Juhan, Deane, *Job's Body*, Barrytown, NY: Barrytown/Station Hill Press, 2003.

Keleman, Stanley, *Your Body Speaks Its Mind*, Berkeley, CA: Center Press, 1981.

Langer, Ellen, *On Becoming an Artist*, New York: Ballantine, 2005.

Leggett, Trevor, *The Dragon Mask*, London: Ippon Books, 1995.

Lowenthal, Wolfe, *There Are No Secrets: Professor Cheng Man-ch'ing and his Tai Chi Chuan*, Berkeley, CA: North Atlantic Books, 1991.

Lowry, Dave, *Traditions: Essays on the Japanese Martial Arts and Ways*, Boston: Tuttle, 2002.

Mead, Margaret, *Male and Female: A Study of the Sexes in a Changing World*, New York: William Morrow & Company, Inc., 1955.

O'Brien, Jess, editor., *Nei Jia Quan: Internal Martial Arts*, Berkeley, CA: North Atlantic Books, 2004.

Pohl, Otto, "Improving the Way Humans Walk," *New York Times*, March 12, 2002.

Sagan, Carl; edited by Ann Druyan, *The Varieties of Scientific Experience*, New York: Penguin Books, 2006.

Schiffmann, Erich, *Yoga: The Spirit and Practice of Moving Into Stillness*, New York: Pocket Books, 1996.

Merton, Thomas, *Hidden Ground of Love: The Letters of Thomas Merton on Relgious Experience and Social Concerns*, edited by William H. Shannon, New York: Farrar, Straus and Giroux, 1985.

Smith, Robert W., *Martial Musings: A Portrayal of the Martial Arts in the 20th Century*, Erie, PA: Via Media, 1999.

Waitzkin, Josh, *The Art of Learning: A Journey in the Pursuit of Excellence*, New York: Free Press, 2007.

Walsch, Neale Donald, *Conversations With God*, New York: Putnam, 1996.

Watts, Alan, "A Cure for Education," from *Talking Zen*, excerpted in *Mountains are Mountains and Rivers are Rivers: Applying Eastern Teachings to Everyday Life*, edited by Ilana Rabinowitz, New York: Hyperion, 1999.

Watts, Alan, *The Culture of Counter Culture: The Edited Transcripts*, Boston: C.E. Tuttle Co., 1998.

Weinzweig, Ari, *Zingerman's Guide to Good Eating*, New York: Houghton Mifflin, 2003.

Wildman, Frank, *Change Your Age: Using Your Body and Brain to Feel Younger, Stronger, and More Fit*, Cambridge, MA: Da Capo Lifelong, 2010.

Zander, Rosamund Stone & Benjamin Zander, *The Art of Possibility: Transforming Professional and Personal Life*, New York: Penguin, 2002.

# Acknowledgements

It is difficult to have "firsts" and "lasts" when talking about people who have touched your life, but linear space-time requires order so here goes…

First, I want thank my parents, Lucy Cha Yu and Francis Yu, who have persevered through many years of dealing with their most difficult child, and in doing so provided him with a humbling example of selfless love, generosity, compassion and loyalty. Only in middle age have I finally come to realize how rare is their embodiment of integrity, commitment and decency—not just as parents, but as human beings. I am still learning from their example.

I want to extend a heart-felt thank you to my main editor and the first of my three main collaborators, Julia Gillam, who single-handedly inspired me to re-edit my '07 manuscript after it had been sitting on the shelf, untouched for over three years. While her genuine interest and unwavering encouragement gave me the necessary spark to dive back into a project I had long ago forsaken, Julia's exquisite sense of style and remarkable insight into human behavior, along with her no-nonsense approach, lent me great confidence in any advice she shared (how lucky I've been to work with a real poet and novelist!).

The first manuscript would never have landed in Julia's hands had it not been for my sister, co-editor and second collaborator, Ann Yu. In '06, Ann persuaded me not to give up on this "running book idea" (I began writing back in '04), while becoming the first to read my '07 manuscript. Thanks to her editorial acumen and our shared belief that mastery comes from methodical plodding over long periods of time, persistence has become a major theme in this final draft. Along with her insightful critique of the text, Ann has lent her wonderful sense of aesthetics to the cover design.

Enlisting my photographer and final collaborator, Andre Andreev, feels like an incredible stroke of luck considering his level of expertise, professionalism and dedication. His aesthetic sense can be seen in the cover design as well as the layout of the entire book. Perhaps the most striking aspect of Andre's work is his methodical scrutiny of every detail. In the fast-paced, time-is-money world of Los Angeles, Andre never showed hurriedness or impatience despite being in the constant throes of sleep deprivation. He always listened to my thoughts and freely expressed his own without the slightest hint of needing to "get it over with." You can find his work at www.loveyourportrait.com.

Obviously, Master Xueyi Li and Master Guoliang Ge have played a pivotal role in getting me to slow down and pay attention. Without their painstaking guidance, I would probably never have discovered what it really means to learn. Their example of unwavering integrity, generosity, patience and persistent wonder continue to inspire me. Through these men, I've come to realize that the best role models are not necessarily the burly fellows we see on the silver screen sorting out the bad guys, but normal people who in everyday life, honor those around them with attentiveness, decency and authenticity.

Along with the masters, I would like to thank their wives, whom I respectfully refer to as, "Shimu" (in Chinese, it is the female term for "master"). Where Master Li and Master Ge have provided me fatherly love and guidance during my time in China, Shimu Li and Shimu Ge have shown me motherly warmth and a soft complement to my masters' "old-school" ways.

Charles Eisenstein has been the most enduring positive influence in my life for the last ten or more years. He was the first person to encourage me to follow my desire—way back when I was an undergrad, and later when I became interested in Feldenkrais and martial arts—and happens to be one of the very few people from my generation to embody the sort of unyielding commitment, accountability and courage that I see in masters of the older generation. More than anyone else, Chuck continues to bring me back to the best parts of myself.

Frank Wildman, my primary Feldenkrais teacher, has introduced remarkable ingenuity into the teaching of the Method. I have lifted many ideas from him, bringing them into both my teaching and writing (some of them appear in this book).

Finally, I would like to extend thanks to the people who have inadvertently planted the seeds for this book: Nancy Angelo, Emily Simon and Sally Searles for encouraging me and giving me precious opportunities to teach; Master Don Schule, whose teachings on Taichi and life have left a deep and lasting impression; My Bagua brother, Pengfu Yuan, who spent many hours teaching me the fundamentals of martial arts; Ann & Chong-Tuo Shi, Yuming Huang, Jiangzhong Teng, Egin Lika, Brenda Generasio Yu & Peter Yu, Sarah Bellestri Shih & Ping Shih, Dawei Ge, Rosmarie Hausherr, Jessica & Neal Plotnick, Marika

Brown Kaplan & Marc Kaplan, Peter McInerney, Jose Luis Fernando Garcia, Michelle Drerup, Corey Bertcher, Al & Avis Jones and Susan Buchan, all of whom graciously housed me during various periods of study; My first martial arts teachers, Yin Xie and Ying Shui, who attempted to teach this old (and stiff) dog new tricks; Dogo (Stephen Backaus) who introduced me to Feldenkrais back in 1994 and lent me the book on the subject which would forever change my life; Master Wuxing Chen and Victor Kan for their generosity and patience in teaching me Chen-style Taichi; Professor Guoguang Mu and Yuan Xiang Chi for giving me my first opportunity to work in China; Marilyn Shoboken, Larry & Maya Spence, Boyan Brodaric, Gail Macdonald, Jim Eisenstein for braving my first Feldenkrais classes; Joseph Del Real and Tony Lasbeur, for giving me a good "reality check," and generously teaching as much kickboxing and boxing as this beginner could absorb in a short period; all of my Bagua "uncles" and "brothers" in Tianjin for their warmth and sharing; Tye Kirk for being a willing guinea pig; Stacy Rowe, Apinya Pokachqiyapat, Angela Anthony, Teri Carter, Susan & Elmo Morales, Cindy Cope, Peg Bravo, Tina Konrath, Todd Hershbine, Anne Mascelli, Jamie Taylor, Lauri Ashworth, Barbie Bayliss, Christopher Riles, Pat Barragan, Mark Pierre, Pam Glenert, Laurence Whitmore and Lidia Magarian for giving me more teaching opportunities; Dr. Xianyong Dong, Dr. Huiling Wang and the rest of my teachers, tutors and classmates at Nankai University and the Tianjin College of Traditional Medicine—you showed me the real meaning of patience and generosity; Sam Payne for thoughtful comments on the 2007 draft; "last" (and just as vital as the "first"), all of my students—unknowingly, you have provided a vast space for me to learn and grow.

# About the Author

Edward Yu is a Certified Feldenkrais Practitioner[sm] and 7th generation lineage holder of Gao Bagua under Masters Guoliang Ge and Xueyi Li.

From his early 20s to his late 30s, Edward took frequent hiatus from his lucrative career as a pizza delivery driver/rider and perpetual grad student to teach English in China, Taiwan and Japan. During his time overseas, he studied Taichi and Bagua, along with Traditional Chinese Medicine at the Tianjin College of Traditional Chinese Medicine. To supplement his Bagua, Edward has also studied enough Thai kickboxing, Western boxing and judo to know that it is sometimes better to run for your life.

Edward's interest in how people learn and process information has led him to bring the disparate fields of martial arts, dance, kinesiology, somatics, psychology, cognitive science and physical education into both his teaching and writing. The impetus for The Art of Slowing Down, for example, came years after Edward quit running and triathloning and discovered that conventional approaches to training are not so effective in turning people into better athletes (though they are quite effective in making them discouraged and neurotic).

In his free time Edward likes to roll around on the floor, walk in circles and stare into space. He also relishes in the fact that he no longer delivers pizzas but instead, spends his time getting other people to roll around on the floor, walk in circles and stare into space.

Breinigsville, PA USA
06 November 2010
248778BV00002B/2/P